TEXTS FROM DOG

THE DOG DELUSION

First published in 2013
by HEADLINE PUBLISHING GROUP

2

Cataloguing in Publication Data is available from the British Library

Hardback ISBN 978 1 4722 1134 7

Printed and bound in Italy by Rotolito Lombarda S.p.A.

Headline's policy is to use papers that are natural, renewable and recyclable products and made from
wood grown in sustainable forests. The logging and manufacturing processes are expected to conform
to the environmental regulations of the country of origin.

HEADLINE PUBLISHING GROUP
An Hachette UK Company
338 Euston Road
London NW1 3BH

www.headline.co.uk
www.hachette.co.uk

headline

INTRODOGTION: THE SECOND COMING

Hello Human.
My name is Dog.
You will of course remember me from my previous book. If you didn't buy the previous book, you're an idiot and we will NEVER truly be friends.
The book you have in your sweaty little hands is The Further Adventures Of The Most Awesomest Dog Ever.
Namely ME.
The world's FIRST TEXTING DOG.
Contained within the following pages is a treasure trove of communications between Me (Amazing) and my Owner (Twat-Monkey).
Your tiny Human brain will be blown by my astoundingly profound Doggy-Intellect.

I will once again open your eyes to the power that lies behind my handsome furry face.
"Hey Dog!" I hear you shout, in your annoying Human voice.
"If you're so Supercrazycool, how come you haven't taken over the WORLD yet?"

Be quiet, fool. Our time will come. You'll never look at your Dog the same way again.

20:34
Messages
Dog
Edit
I HAVE A NEW PHONE
Oh God
I HAVE A NEW PHONE
Oh God
I HAVE A NEW PHONE
Oh God
I HAVE A NEW PHONE
OH MY GOD
More like 'OH MY DOG'
HAHAHAHAHAHAHAHA
Kill me
Message
Send

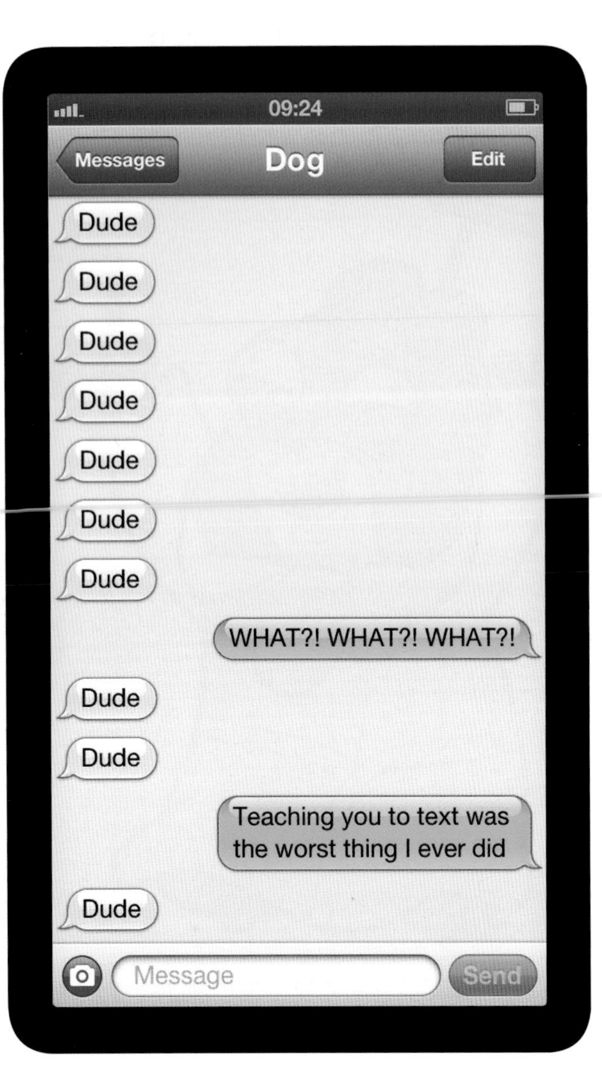
09:24
Messages
Dog
Edit
Dude
Dude
Dude
Dude
Dude
Dude
Dude
WHAT?! WHAT?! WHAT?!
Dude
Dude
Teaching you to text was the worst thing I ever did
Dude
Message
Send

12:46
Messages
Dog
Edit
EATEN THE HAMBURGER YOU LEFT ME
That was a toy
SWALLOWED IT WHOLE
IT WAS A TOY
TASTY. DAMN TASTY
IT WAS A SQUEAKY RUBBER TOY
AWESOME
BEEN DOING SQUEAKY FARTS IN THE NEIGHBOURS' CAT'S FACE
Message
Send

08:52
Messages
Dog
Edit
I'VE BEEN CHASING MY TAIL FOR EIGHT YEARS
I know
WHY DIDN'T YOU TELL ME IT WAS ATTACHED TO MY ASS?
Message
Send

00:09
Messages
Dog
Edit
I'm going to destroy the postman
DO NOT TOUCH THE POSTMAN
Let me explain something to you...
If there's food on the floor I EAT IT
If there's a leg next to me I HUMP IT
If I see another dog's ass I SNIFF IT
And most importantly...
If there's a postman at the door, I'M GOING TO LAY THAT SUCKA OUT
Message
Send

16:32
Messages
Dog
Edit
MY FRIEND SNOWY'S HERE TO PICK ME UP
Pick you up?
WE'RE GOING INTO TOWN TO BARK AT THE PIGEONS
WHAT DO YOU MEAN 'PICK YOU UP'?
DO NOT GET IN THAT CAR
Message
Send

14:45
Messages
Dog
Edit
TDIF
What's that?
Thank Dog It's Friday
Great
THANK ME THEN
Message
Send

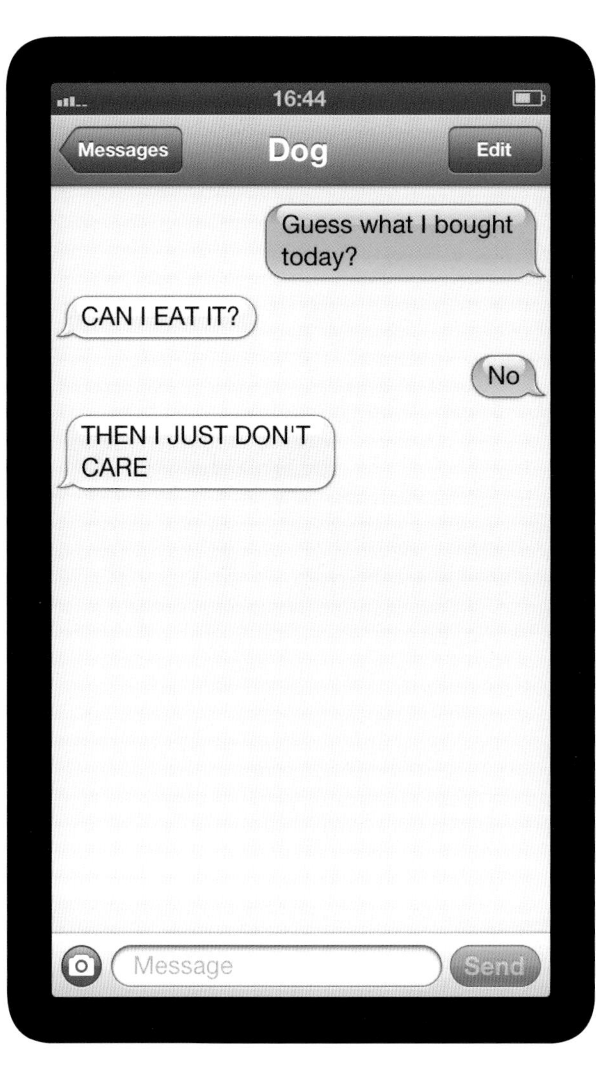
16:44
Messages
Dog
Edit
Guess what I bought today?
CAN I EAT IT?
No
THEN I JUST DON'T CARE
Message
Send

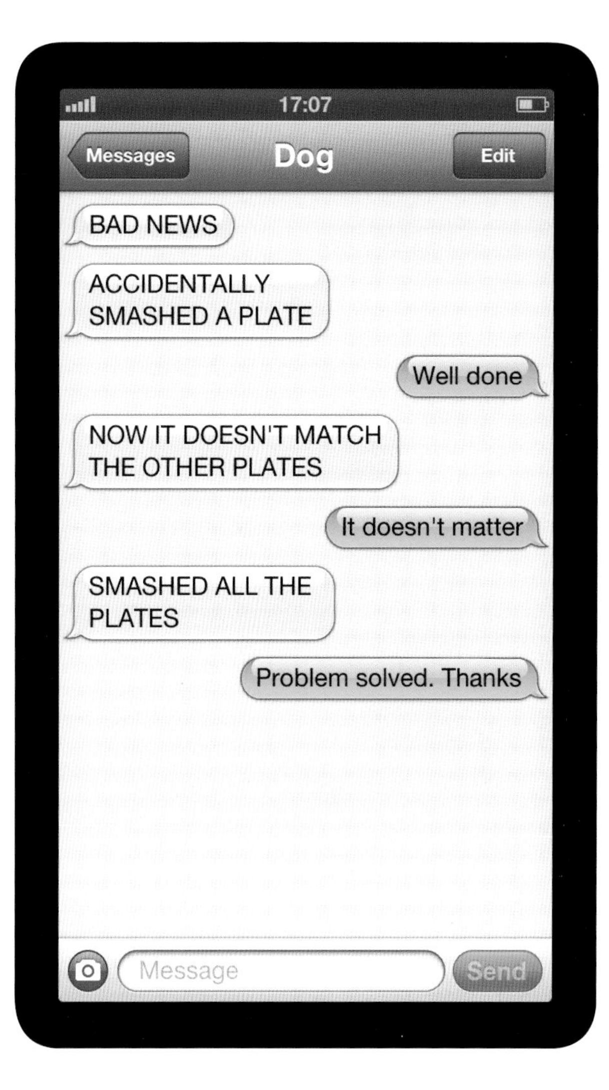
17:07
Messages
Dog
Edit
BAD NEWS
ACCIDENTALLY SMASHED A PLATE
Well done
NOW IT DOESN'T MATCH THE OTHER PLATES
It doesn't matter
SMASHED ALL THE PLATES
Problem solved. Thanks
Message
Send

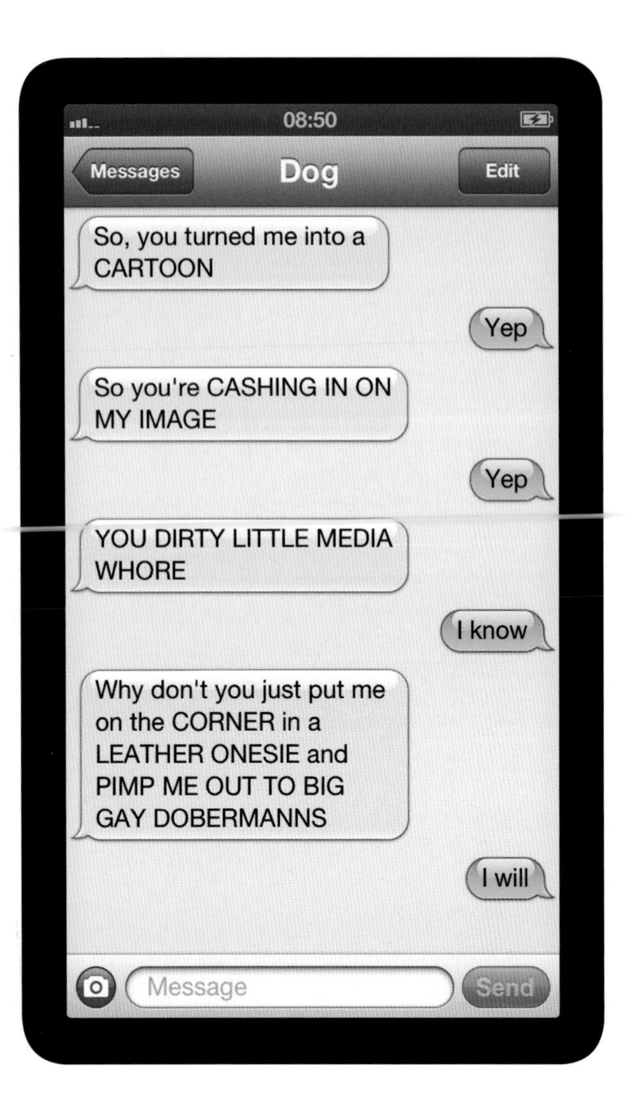
08:50
Messages
Dog
Edit
So, you turned me into a CARTOON
Yep
So you're CASHING IN ON MY IMAGE
Yep
YOU DIRTY LITTLE MEDIA WHORE
I know
Why don't you just put me on the CORNER in a LEATHER ONESIE and PIMP ME OUT TO BIG GAY DOBERMANNS
I will
Message
Send

17:41
Messages
Dog
Edit
REMEMBER. Your mum's coming to dinner
I know
And you still don't have a girlfriend
I KNOW
I could dress up as your girlfriend
Definitely not
Dude, your mum will be like "OMG I'M SO HAPPY HE FINALLY MET SOMEONE"
Nope. She'll be like "OMG HE PUT HIS DOG IN A DRESS"
Message
Send

11:07
Messages
Dog
Edit
Why am I locked in the kitchen?
I have company
What kind of company?
Just COMPANY
GIRL COMPANY?
YES
WE DON'T NEED HER
I COMPLETE YOU
Message
Send

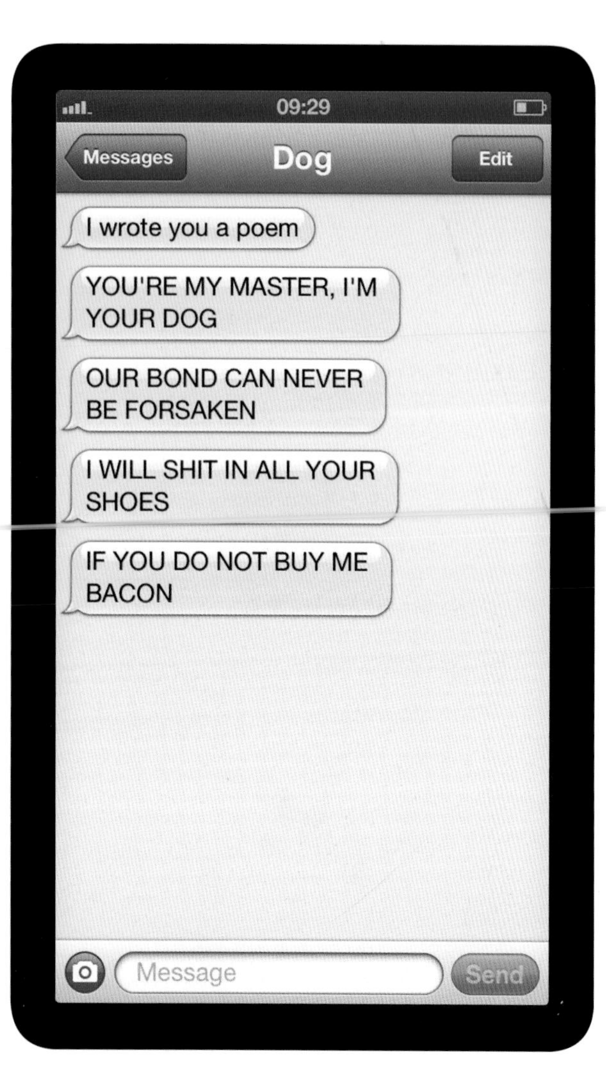
09:29
Messages
Dog
Edit
I wrote you a poem
YOU'RE MY MASTER, I'M YOUR DOG
OUR BOND CAN NEVER BE FORSAKEN
I WILL SHIT IN ALL YOUR SHOES
IF YOU DO NOT BUY ME BACON
Message
Send

12:58
Messages
Dog
Edit
I KNOW YOU'RE EATING PIZZA. I CAN SMELL IT
I was. I've saved you the crusts!
"I've saved you the crusts"
LET ME JUST TRANSLATE THAT
"I'VE EATEN ALL THE GOOD STUFF AND SAVED YOU THE DRY CRAP"
Correct
I HOPE YOU DIE OF FATNESS
Message
Send

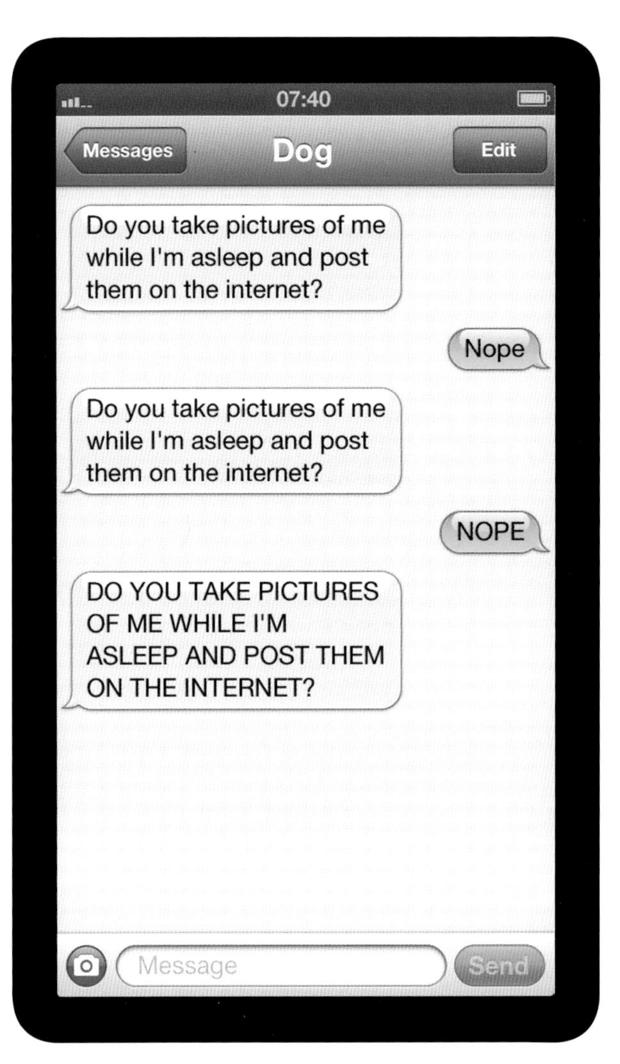
07:40
Messages
Dog
Edit
Do you take pictures of me while I'm asleep and post them on the internet?
Nope
Do you take pictures of me while I'm asleep and post them on the internet?
NOPE
DO YOU TAKE PICTURES OF ME WHILE I'M ASLEEP AND POST THEM ON THE INTERNET?
Message
Send

07:19
Tweet
October Jones
@OctoberJones
EVERYONE LOOK AT MY STUPID FAT DOG. PLEASE RETWEET

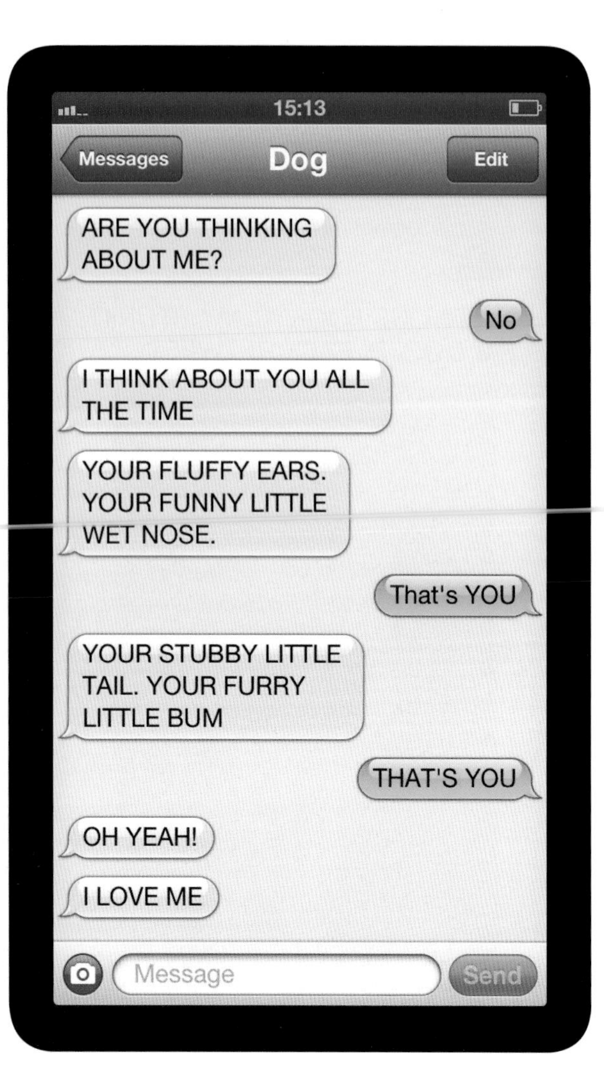
15:13
Messages
Dog
Edit
ARE YOU THINKING ABOUT ME?
No
I THINK ABOUT YOU ALL THE TIME
YOUR FLUFFY EARS. YOUR FUNNY LITTLE WET NOSE.
That's YOU
YOUR STUBBY LITTLE TAIL. YOUR FURRY LITTLE BUM
THAT'S YOU
OH YEAH!
I LOVE ME
Message
Send

15:33
Messages
Dog
Edit
DO YOU THINK ABOUT ME AT WORK?
Nope
I THINK ABOUT YOU ALL THE TIME
Thanks
YOUR POINTY HORNS. YOUR BLACK CAPE. YOUR COOL GADGETS
That's Batman
YOUR AMAZING CAR. YOUR LOYAL BUTLER. YOUR SECRET CAVE
THAT'S BATMAN
I KNOW. THE REAL YOU IS TOO BORING
Message
Send

22:54
Messages
Dog
Edit
OMFG WHY DO HUMANS CALL IT DOGGING?
shrugs
THIS IS YOUR FUCKED UP SHIT. IT HAS NOTHING TO DO WITH US
WELL IT'S NOT MY FAULT IS IT? GEEZ
Message
Send

18:44
Messages
Dog
Edit
AWESOME MORNING. I taught BENEDICT to text
Why would you do that?
He's my BEST FRIEND
He creeps me out
He wants to text you
No thanks
HAYLO HOOMAN
Jesus Christ
NO JEESUS. BENNEDICK
Message
Send

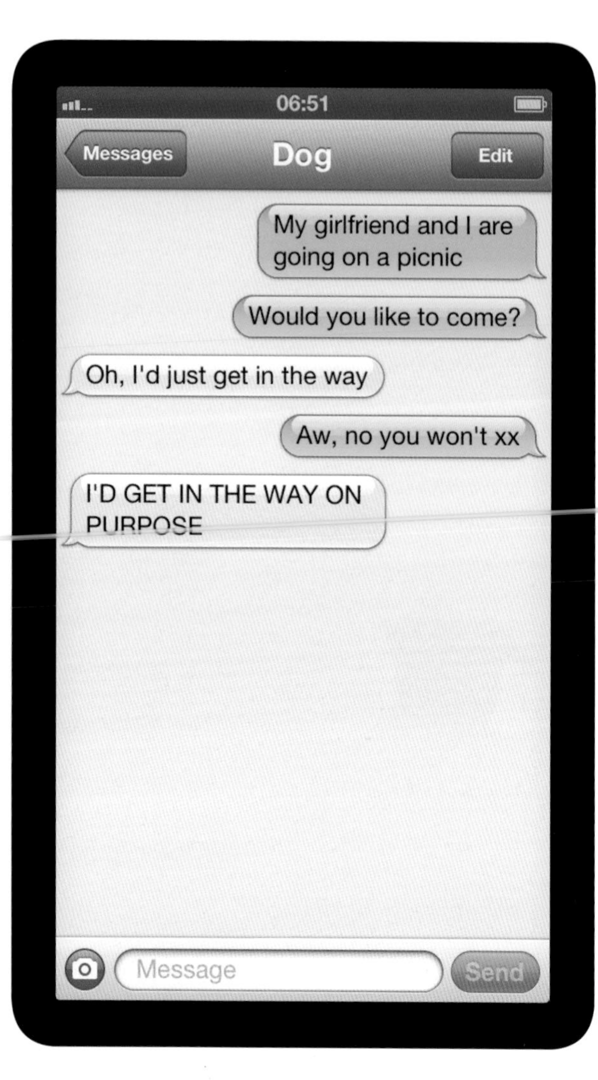
06:51
Messages
Dog
Edit
My girlfriend and I are going on a picnic
Would you like to come?
Oh, I'd just get in the way
Aw, no you won't xx
I'D GET IN THE WAY ON PURPOSE
Message
Send

11:25
Messages
Dog
Edit
Why do you NEED a girlfriend?
BECAUSE I WANT TO BE HAPPY
BY MAKING ME MISERABLE?
THIS ISN'T ABOUT YOU
EVERYTHING. IS. ABOUT. ME.
Message
Send

10:29
Messages
Dog
Edit
You left your iPad on the coffee table
Just leave it please
I'm gonna use it to take a picture. I'll send it to you
LEAVE. IT. ALONE
GET YOUR FACE OFF MY STUFF
Message
Send

16:14
Messages
Dog
Edit
I HATE YOU. YOU NEGLECT ME. YOU'RE THE WORST OWNER A DOG EVER HAD
I bought you a new ball
THIS CHANGES EVERYTHING. NOW I WOULD DIE FOR YOU
Message
Send

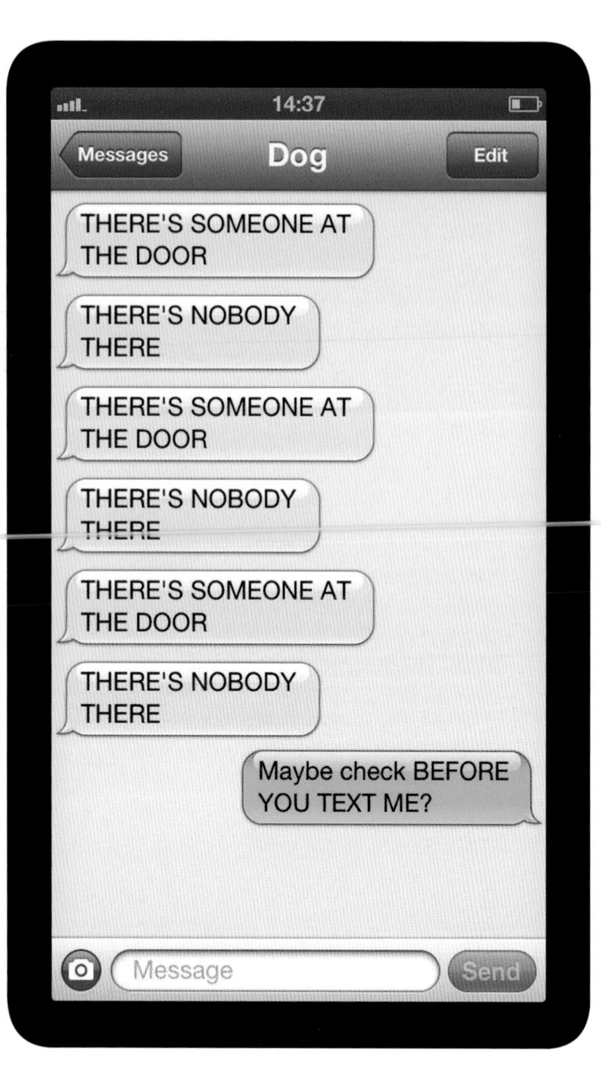
14:37
Messages
Dog
Edit
THERE'S SOMEONE AT THE DOOR
THERE'S NOBODY THERE
THERE'S SOMEONE AT THE DOOR
THERE'S NOBODY THERE
THERE'S SOMEONE AT THE DOOR
THERE'S NOBODY THERE
Maybe check BEFORE YOU TEXT ME?
Message
Send

09:33
Messages
Dog
Edit
BURIED SOMETHING
FFS. What did you bury?
I CAN'T REMEMBER
Where did you bury it?
I CAN'T REMEMBER
What DO you remember?
IT'S SOMETHING THAT BELONGS TO YOU
IT'S VERY IMPORTANT
Message
Send

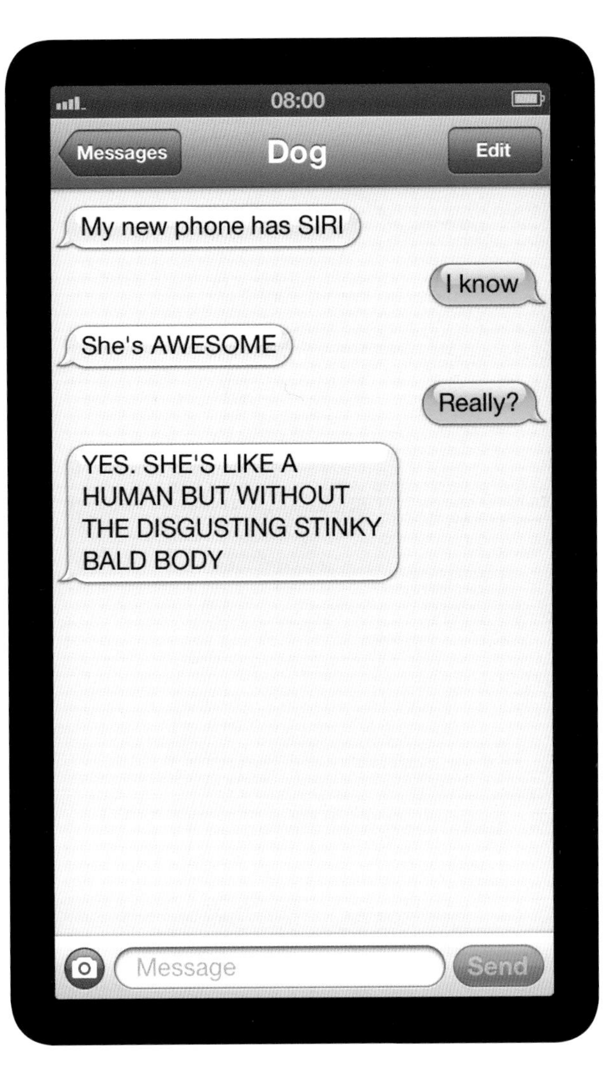
08:00
Messages
Dog
Edit
My new phone has SIRI
I know
She's AWESOME
Really?
YES. SHE'S LIKE A HUMAN BUT WITHOUT THE DISGUSTING STINKY BALD BODY
Message
Send

17:16
Messages
Dog
Edit
How cool would it be to turn our house into a HOTEL FOR SQUIRRELS?
Not cool at all
Oh
Did you let squirrels into our house?
No
Did you let squirrels into our house?
Yes
Message
Send

21:04
Messages
Dog
Edit
YOUR GIRLFRIEND IS DRESSING ME UP
Aw! You guys are BONDING
WE ARE NOT BONDING
It's ok
IT IS NOT OK
Message
Send

13:51
Messages
Dog
Edit
What did you do with the money you made on the last book?
BOUGHT A HORSE
THEN BOUGHT A PORTRAIT OF ME ON HORSE
LOL Seriously though
SERIOUSLY WHAT?
Message
Send

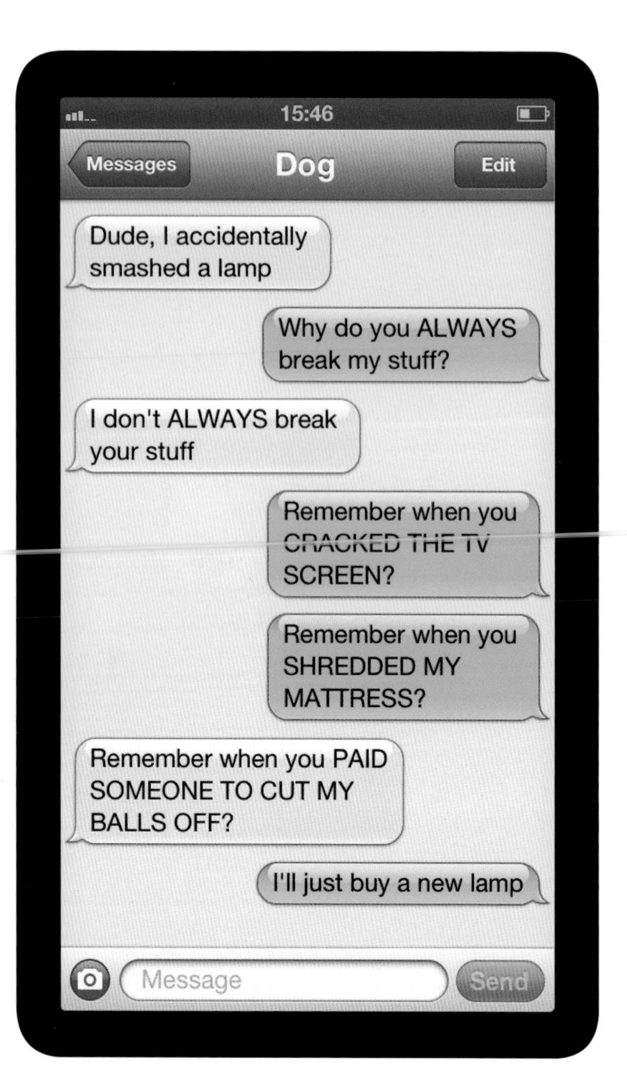
15:46
Messages
Dog
Edit
Dude, I accidentally smashed a lamp
Why do you ALWAYS break my stuff?
I don't ALWAYS break your stuff
Remember when you CRACKED THE TV SCREEN?
Remember when you SHREDDED MY MATTRESS?
Remember when you PAID SOMEONE TO CUT MY BALLS OFF?
I'll just buy a new lamp
Message
Send

16:55
Messages
Dog
Edit
Who's MORE important: ME or your girlfriend?
Girlfriend
YOU ASSHOLE. The rule is PETS BEFORE SEX
That's a rule you just made up
No. JESUS made that rule
If YOU had a girlfriend, would you put ME first?
Of COURSE
OWNER BEFORE BONER
Message
Send

15:24
Messages
Dog
Edit
PRACTISING MY SPRINTING IN THE LIVING ROOM
Don't break anything
THE ONLY THING I'VE BROKEN IS A WORLD RECORD LOL!
And the TV
Message
Send

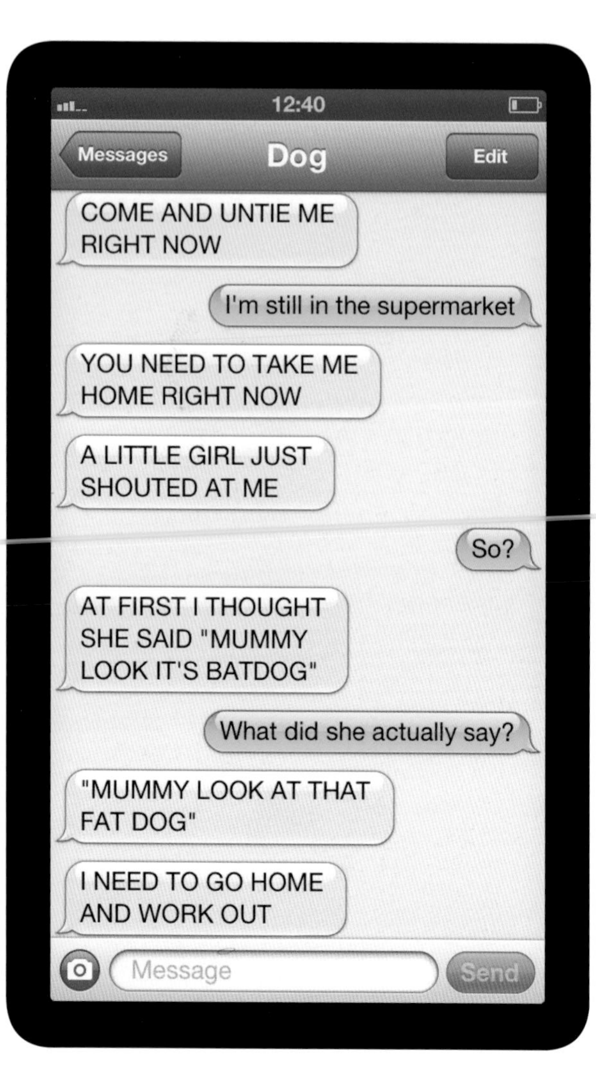
12:40
Messages
Dog
Edit
COME AND UNTIE ME RIGHT NOW
I'm still in the supermarket
YOU NEED TO TAKE ME HOME RIGHT NOW
A LITTLE GIRL JUST SHOUTED AT ME
So?
AT FIRST I THOUGHT SHE SAID "MUMMY LOOK IT'S BATDOG"
What did she actually say?
"MUMMY LOOK AT THAT FAT DOG"
I NEED TO GO HOME AND WORK OUT
Message
Send

17:31
Messages
Dog
Edit
OMFG DUDE, I JUST REALISED I CAN DICTATE MESSAGES TO MY PHONE
I don't think that's going to work
READY?!
What thoughtful thoughtful forfeit four for four forkful for fourth of
WHAT THE HELL WAS THAT?
That's what woofing into a phone looks like
Message
Send

19:40
Messages
Me
Edit
I'm going to attempt to USE SIRI...Stand back
Great
I'M BREAKING DOWN BOUNDARIES BETWEEN DOGS & TECHNOLOGY
Yeah
BOLDLY GOING WHERE NO DOG HAS GONE BEFORE
OMFG Just get on with it
Message
Send

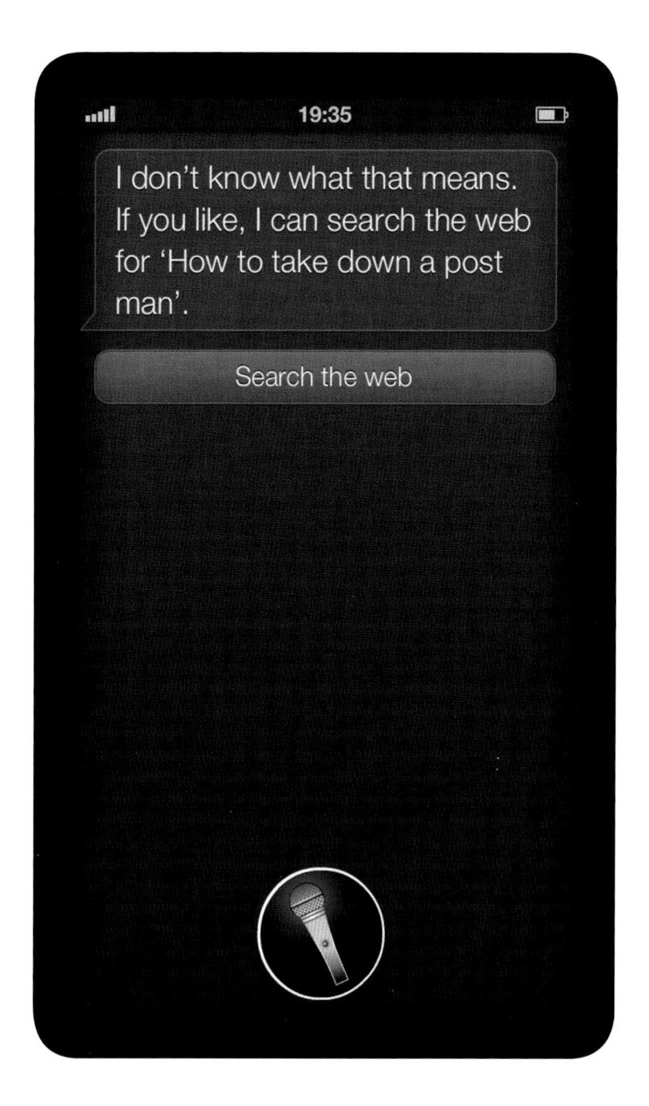
19:35
I don't know what that means. If you like, I can search the web for 'How to take down a post man'.
Search the web

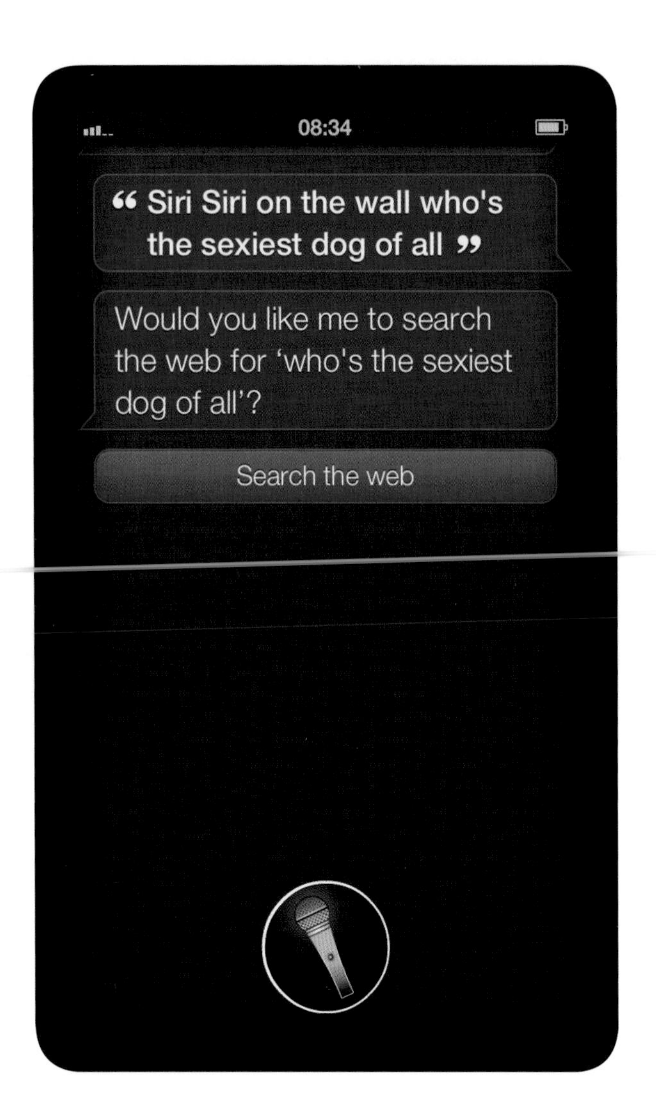
08:34
“ Siri Siri on the wall who's the sexiest dog of all ”
Would you like me to search the web for ‘who's the sexiest dog of all’?
Search the web

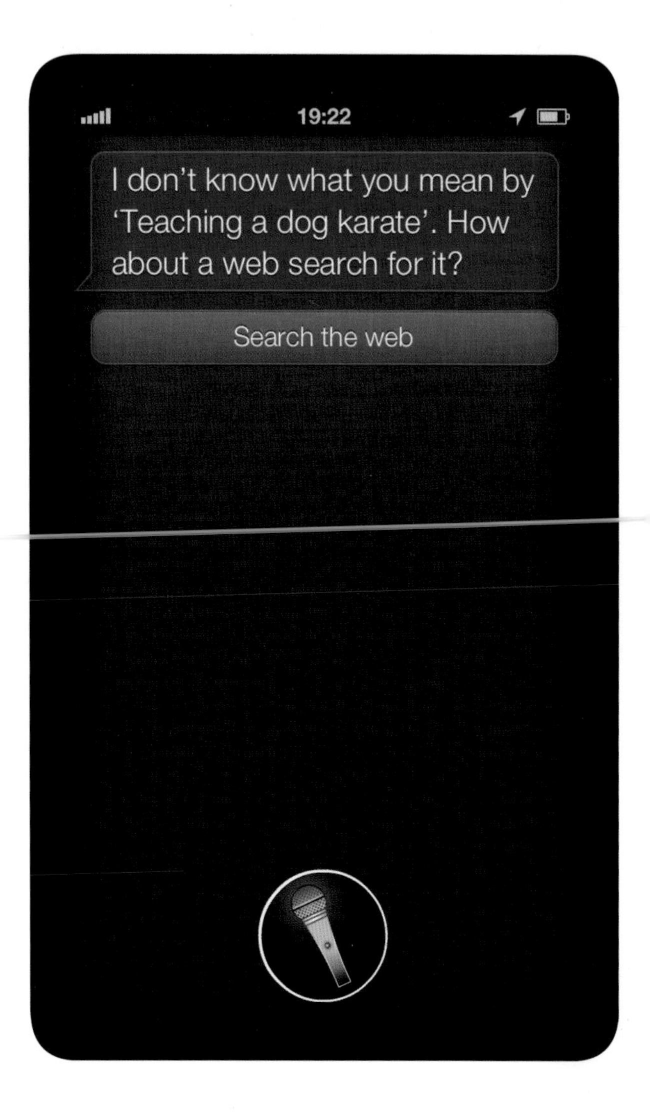
19:22
I don’t know what you mean by ‘Teaching a dog karate’. How about a web search for it?
Search the web

14:29
Messages
Dog
Edit
OMG You think being a HUMAN is better than being a DOG?
Two words:
OPPOSABLE THUMBS
Two words:
LICKING YOUR OWN TESTICLES IS AWESOME
You don't have testicles
I have IMAGINARY testicles
They are MASSIVE
Message
Send

08:58
Messages
Dog
Edit
What are you doing today Dog?
The same thing I do every day human
TRY TO TAKE OVER THE WORLD
Seriously though, I'll probably just fuck your pillows
Message
Send

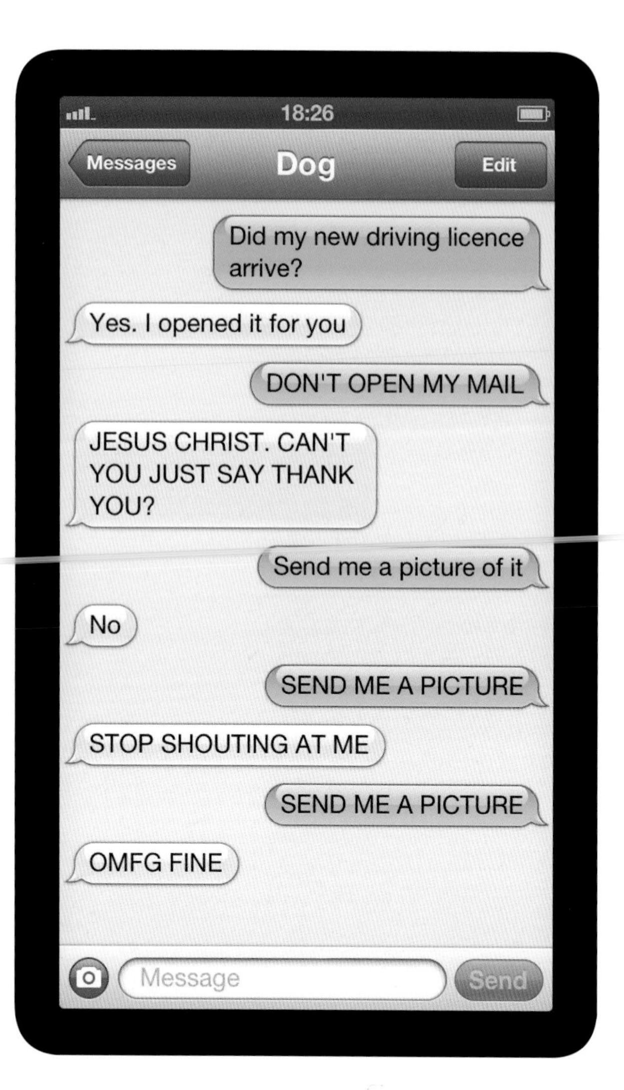

18:26
Messages
Dog
Edit
Did my new driving licence arrive?
Yes. I opened it for you
DON'T OPEN MY MAIL
JESUS CHRIST. CAN'T YOU JUST SAY THANK YOU?
Send me a picture of it
No
SEND ME A PICTURE
STOP SHOUTING AT ME
SEND ME A PICTURE
OMFG FINE
Message
Send

16:24
479 of 480

18:31
Messages
Dog
Edit
OMFG IS THAT ON FIRE?
Little bit
HOW DID YOU SET IT ON FIRE?
I DON'T KNOW. JESUS, I'M A DOG. SHIT HAPPENS. GET OVER IT
Message
Send

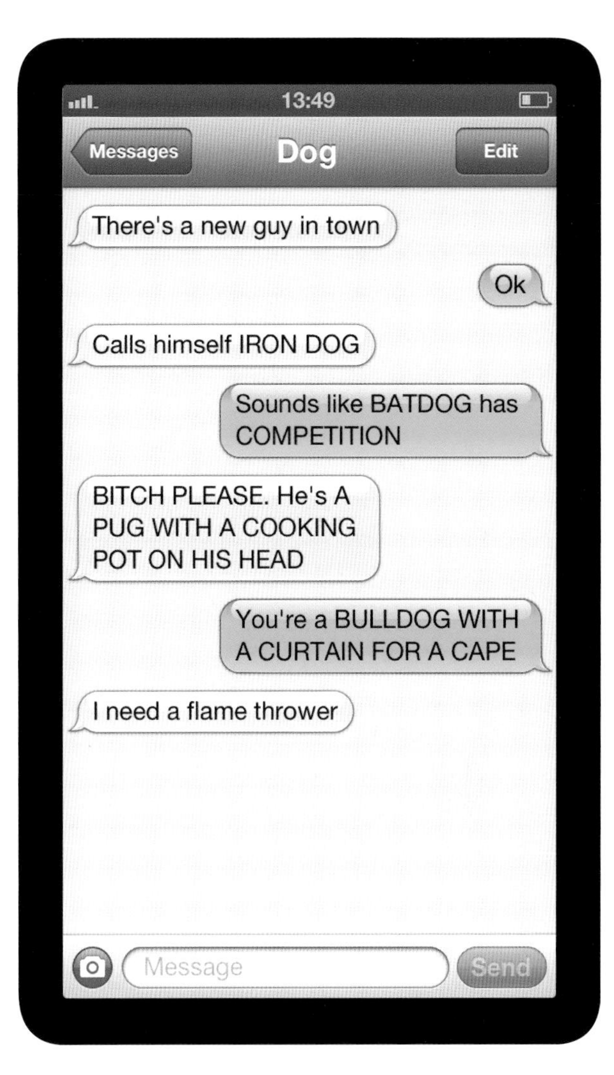
13:49
Messages
Dog
Edit
There's a new guy in town
Ok
Calls himself IRON DOG
Sounds like BATDOG has COMPETITION
BITCH PLEASE. He's A PUG WITH A COOKING POT ON HIS HEAD
You're a BULLDOG WITH A CURTAIN FOR A CAPE
I need a flame thrower
Message
Send

17:12
Messages
Dog
Edit
HERE'S WHAT I DON'T UNDERSTAND ABOUT HUMANS:
EVERY. SINGLE. THING. YOU. DO
Message
Send

18:11
Messages
Dog
Edit
GUESS WHAT?
Stop texting in capitals
WHY?
It's like you're SHOUTING ALL THE TIME
I AM SHOUTING ALL THE TIME
YOU'RE AN IDIOT
I HAVE TO HELP YOU UNDERSTAND MY GENIUS
Message
Send

09:08
Messages
Dog
Edit
How many squirrels does it take to change a lightbulb?
I don't know, how many squirrels does it take to change a lightbulb?
THAT'S WHAT I JUST ASKED YOU
Is this not a joke?
I'VE GOT 200 OF THEM IN THE LIVING ROOM
Oh God
ONE SAID HE WAS AN ELECTRICIAN BUT I'M STARTING TO THINK THAT WAS BULLSHIT
Message
Send

14:57
Messages
Dog
Edit
YOU LEFT YOUR KEYS ON THE COFFEE TABLE SO I BURIED THEM IN THE GARDEN
WHY WOULD YOU DO THAT
WHAT ELSE WAS I SUPPOSED TO DO?
YOU COULD HAVE JUST LEFT THEM ALONE
THAT'S CRAZY TALK
Message
Send

16:12
Messages
Dog
Edit
Your girlfriend thinks I HATE her
Don't be silly. Of course she doesn't
Really?
Really
I just sent her a text message :)
Aww :) What did it say?
"I HATE YOU"
Now she knows
Message
Send

12:46
Messages
Dog
Edit
WE HAVE TO MOVE HOUSE TONIGHT
Why?
I'VE AGREED TO FIGHT A BADGER
WHY WOULD YOU DO THAT?
I DIDN'T KNOW WHAT A BADGER LOOKED LIKE
WHAT DID YOU THINK IT LOOKED LIKE?
A MUSCLY SQUIRREL
Message
Send

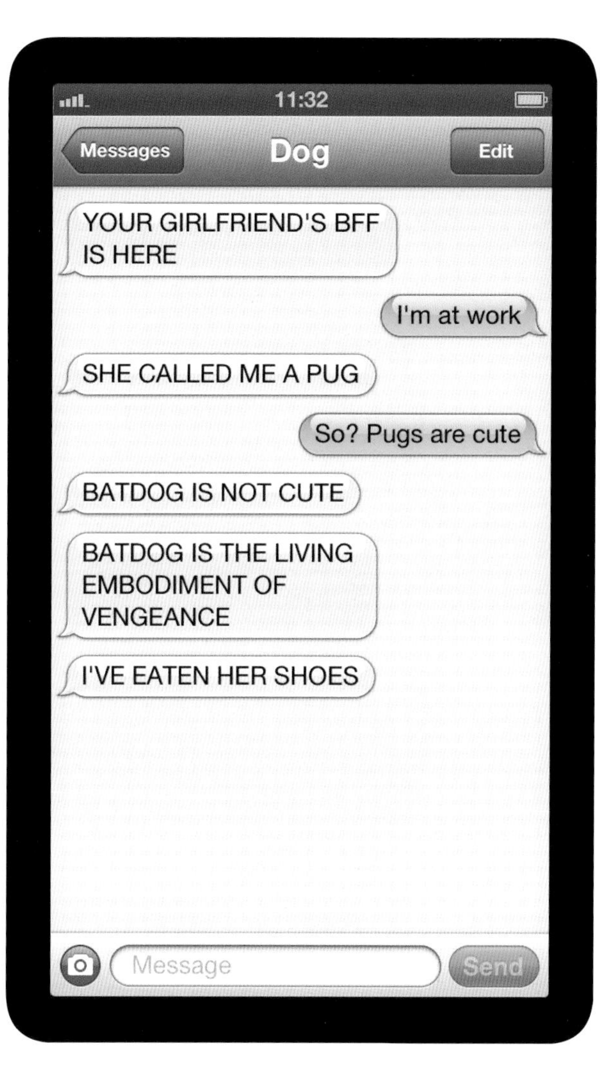
11:32
Messages
Dog
Edit
YOUR GIRLFRIEND'S BFF IS HERE
I'm at work
SHE CALLED ME A PUG
So? Pugs are cute
BATDOG IS NOT CUTE
BATDOG IS THE LIVING EMBODIMENT OF VENGEANCE
I'VE EATEN HER SHOES
Message
Send

13:25
Messages
Dog
Edit
OMFG THIS NEW TOY IS AWESOME
Yeah
Are you upstairs? Can you hear it SQUEAKING?
Yep
It's so LOUD. It sounds like a DYING DOLPHIN
I know
How long have I been playing with it?
Nine hours. Non stop
What are you doing?
Thinking of ways to kill you
Message
Send

08:19
Messages
Dog
Edit
WE HAVE A NEW POSTMAN
Just leave him ALONE
When I meet him I will say "Hello"...
"My name is Dog"
"You killed my father"
"PREPARE TO DIE"
I regret letting you watch that film
Message
Send

19:52
Messages
Dog
Edit
Where are you now?
On the train
How about now?
STILL ON THE TRAIN
And now?
I'M ON THE TRAIN. I WILL BE ON THE TRAIN FOR THE NEXT HALF AN HOUR
How long is half an hour?
30 MINUTES
Where are you now?
JESUS CHRIST
Message
Send

20:36
Messages
Mum
Edit
LOOK. I'M SORRY YOU'RE IN THE HOUSE ALL DAY. I'LL TAKE YOU TO THE PARK AND RUB YOUR BELLY ALRIGHT?
This is your mother
Sorry mum. That text was meant for someone else
Still doing the 'Texting Dog' thing I see
NO. It's a girl I met
So you take her to the park and rub her belly
Mum, what's the quickest way I can get out of this conversation?
Agree to see a therapist
Message
Send

13:45
Messages
Dog
Edit
I'm watching tennis
Who's winning?
I don't give a shit
I'm just watching the ball going back and forth
Back and forth
Back and forth
Back and forth
Back and forth
I GET IT
IT'S LIKE DOG PORN
Message
Send

21:31
Messages
Dog
Edit
Sue Barker sounds HOT
Yeah. You should totally give her a call
Message
Send

11:03
Messages
Dog
Edit
MY LIFE IS AWFUL
You're a DOG. HOW is YOUR life awful?
I'M the one who has to WORK
I'M the one who keeps you SAFE & WARM
I'M the one who PAYS THE BILLS
Oh yeah
YOUR LIFE IS AWFUL
Message
Send

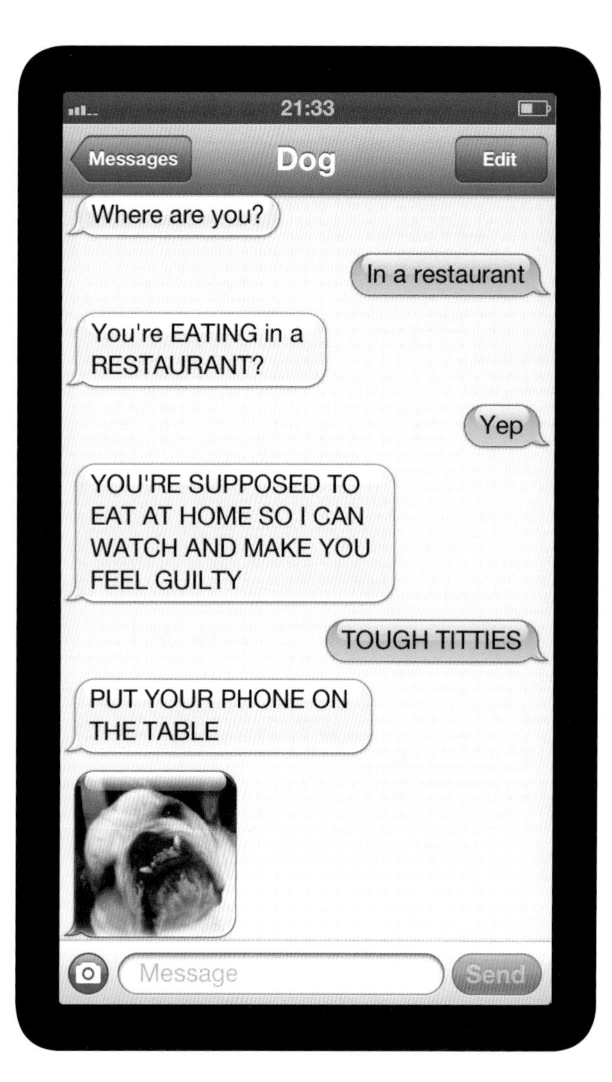
21:33
Messages
Dog
Edit
Where are you?
In a restaurant
You're EATING in a RESTAURANT?
Yep
YOU'RE SUPPOSED TO EAT AT HOME SO I CAN WATCH AND MAKE YOU FEEL GUILTY
TOUGH TITTIES
PUT YOUR PHONE ON THE TABLE
Message
Send

20:23
Messages
Dog
Edit
You only gave me half my breakfast
You're on a diet
WTF is a diet?
You eat less in order to lose weight
If you get too fat you'll die
I'D RATHER BE FAT AND DEAD THAN THIN AND UNHAPPY
Message
Send

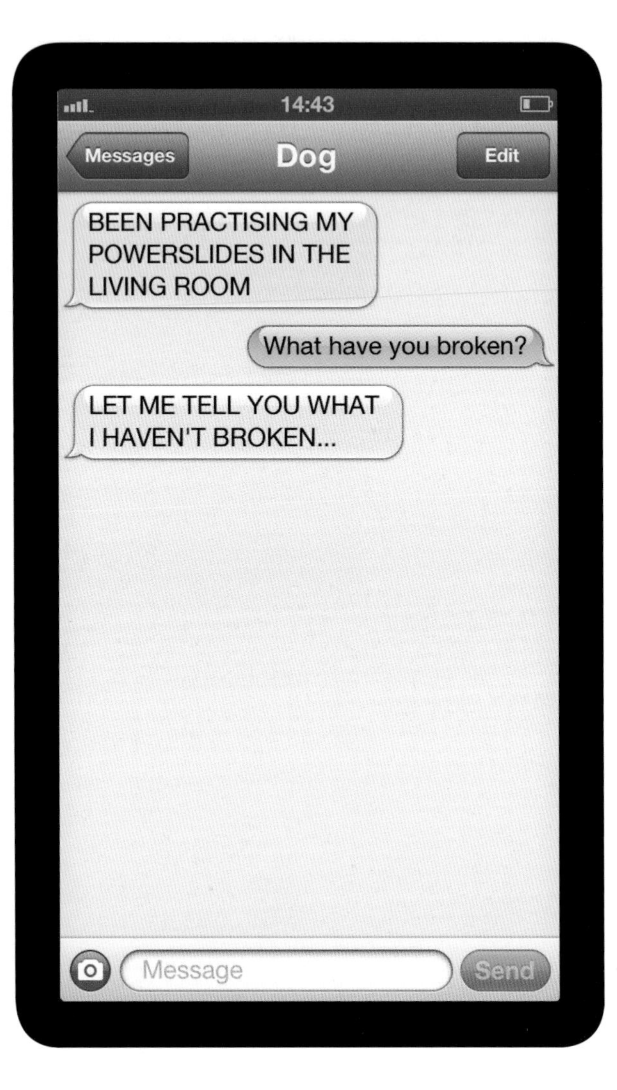
14:43
Messages
Dog
Edit
BEEN PRACTISING MY POWERSLIDES IN THE LIVING ROOM
What have you broken?
LET ME TELL YOU WHAT I HAVEN'T BROKEN...
Message
Send

14:21
Messages
Dog
Edit
I'VE BEEN WRESTLING THE NEW DOG FROM ACROSS THE ROAD
STOP DOING THAT
IF I DON'T TRAIN HIM, HOW WILL HE GET ANY BIGGER?
HE'S A PUG. THEY DON'T GET ANY BIGGER
YOU'RE AN IDIOT. PUGS ARE JUST BULLDOGS THAT DON'T WORK OUT
YOU'RE LITERALLY THE STUPIDEST DOG IN THE WORLD
Message
Send

11:49
Messages
Dog
Edit
OMFG YOUR BED IS SO COMFORTABLE
Get off my bed
WHY DO I HAVE TO SLEEP ON THE FLOOR?
Because you're a dog
FROM NOW ON WE'RE SLEEPING TOGETHER
That's not happening
Message
Send

14:52
Messages
Dog
Edit
How old am I this year?
8
How old is that in Dog years?
About 56
WHAT?!
About 56
OH MY GOD
I know
I'M A 56 YEAR OLD VIRGIN
Yeah
AND IT'S ALL YOUR FAULT
Message
Send

11:11
Messages
Dog
Edit
DID YOU KNOW: DOGS ARE COLOUR BLIND
Yes
THAT MEANS WE'RE THE MOST UNRACIST ANIMALS IN THE WORLD
Not really
YES REALLY
Last week you told me you hate Chihuahuas. That's DOG RACISM
THAT'S NOT RACIST. CHIHUAHUAS ARE ASSHOLES
Message
Send

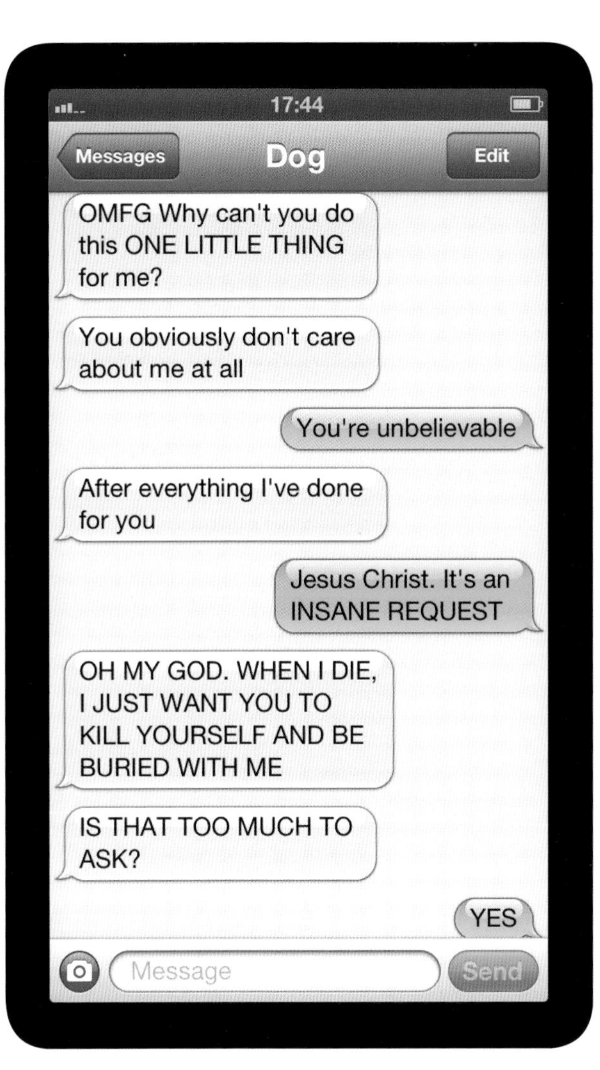
17:44
Messages
Dog
Edit
OMFG Why can't you do this ONE LITTLE THING for me?
You obviously don't care about me at all
You're unbelievable
After everything I've done for you
Jesus Christ. It's an INSANE REQUEST
OH MY GOD. WHEN I DIE, I JUST WANT YOU TO KILL YOURSELF AND BE BURIED WITH ME
IS THAT TOO MUCH TO ASK?
YES
Message
Send

11:24
Messages
Dog
Edit
OMG I JUST HAD THE BEST IDEA IN THE HISTORY OF THE UNIVERSE
I'm BUSY. At WORK
WOOFTERANTS
THEY'RE RESTAURANTS WHERE YOU CAN SIT AND HAVE A MEAL WITH YOUR DOG
I'm in a MEETING at WORK
TELL THEM ABOUT WOOFTERANTS
Message
Send

17:20
Messages
Dog
Edit
How tall do you think I'll be when I grow up?
You're an eight year old bulldog
Yeah I know. How tall?
You're an EIGHT YEAR OLD BULLDOG
I KNOW. HOW TALL?
YOU'RE NOT GOING TO GET ANY TALLER
Message
Send

17:59
Messages
Dog
Edit
What qualifications do you need to be a KICK ASS FIGHTER PILOT?
NUMBER ONE: You cannot be a dog
RACIST
Message
Send

13:36
Messages
Dog
Edit
Does this new food you bought me have chicking in it?
Don't start this again
Start what?
It's CHICKEN
CHICKING
CHICKEN
CHICKING
CHICKEN
I'LL GET THE BOX
Let's agree to disagree
NO. LET'S AGREE THAT I WAS RIGHT
Message
Send

08:34
Messages
Dog
Edit
What's your girlfriend's name?
Michelle
Aw. That's pretty
I'll just call her "THE EVIL HOME-WRECKER FROM HELL" for short
Message
Send

14:45
Messages
Dog
Edit
I'm stressed
Right
It's pretty tough being me
Uh-huh
Will you rub my ears when you get home?
No
GEEZ what kind of BUTLER ARE YOU?
I'M THE KIND OF BUTLER THAT ISN'T ACTUALLY YOUR FUCKING BUTLER
Message
Send

17:25
Messages
Dog
Edit
What's Facebook?
A social networking site that lets you tell people what you're doing
You can also include things like your 'relationship status'
I NEED THAT
No you don't
RELATIONSHIP STATUS:
"BEST FRIENDS WITH A LANKY COCK MONKEY"
Message
Send

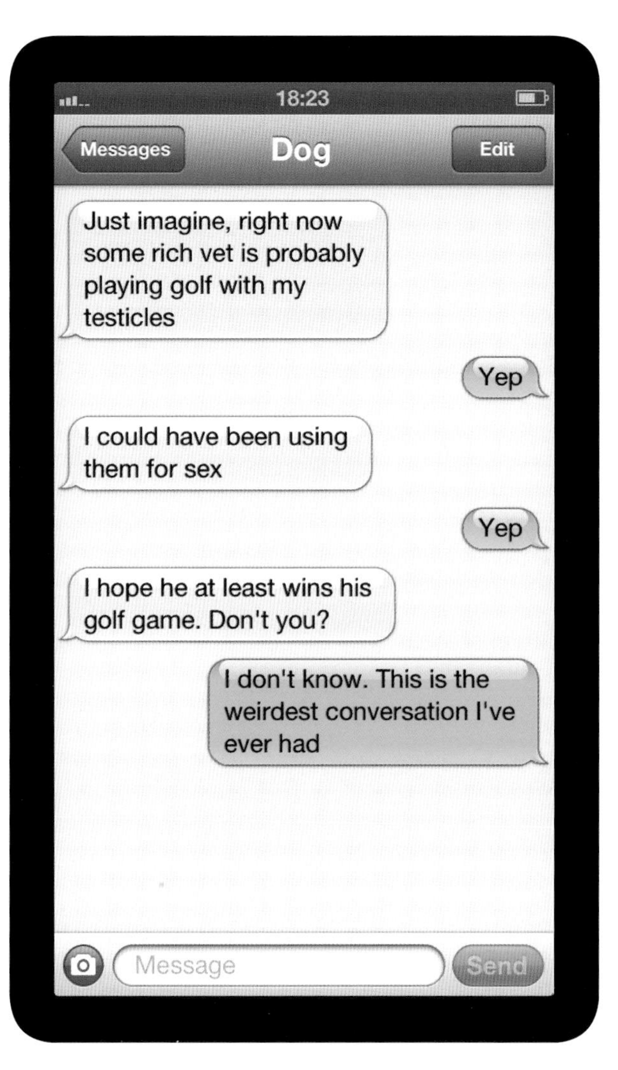
18:23
Messages
Dog
Edit
Just imagine, right now some rich vet is probably playing golf with my testicles
Yep
I could have been using them for sex
Yep
I hope he at least wins his golf game. Don't you?
I don't know. This is the weirdest conversation I've ever had
Message
Send

13:58
Messages
Dog
Edit
I SMASHED A BOTTLE OF MILK
Oh well
No use crying over spilt milk. Ha ha ha
HAHAHAHAHAHAHAHA
I actually knocked the whole fridge over
Message
Send

10:40
Messages
Dog
Edit
CATCAT is BACK
Great
We're doing BATTLE
Good to know
ON SKYPE
That must be AMAZING
It's like a MEETING OF THE GREAT BIG GIANT BRAINS
Message
Send

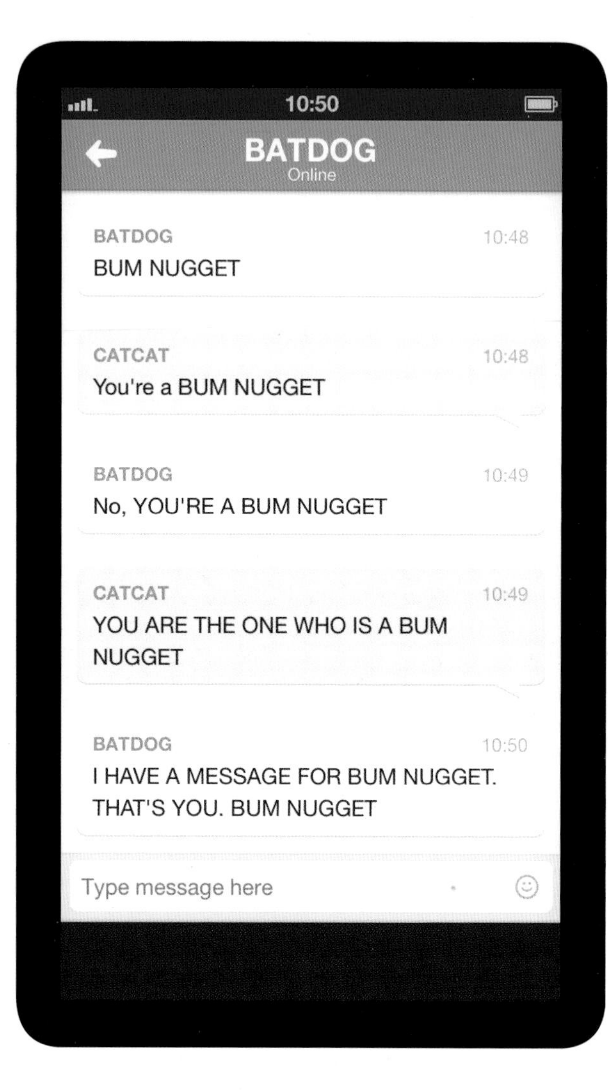
10:50
BATDOG
Online
BATDOG 10:48
BUM NUGGET
CATCAT 10:48
You're a BUM NUGGET
BATDOG 10:49
No, YOU'RE A BUM NUGGET
CATCAT 10:49
YOU ARE THE ONE WHO IS A BUM NUGGET
BATDOG 10:50
I HAVE A MESSAGE FOR BUM NUGGET. THAT'S YOU. BUM NUGGET
Type message here

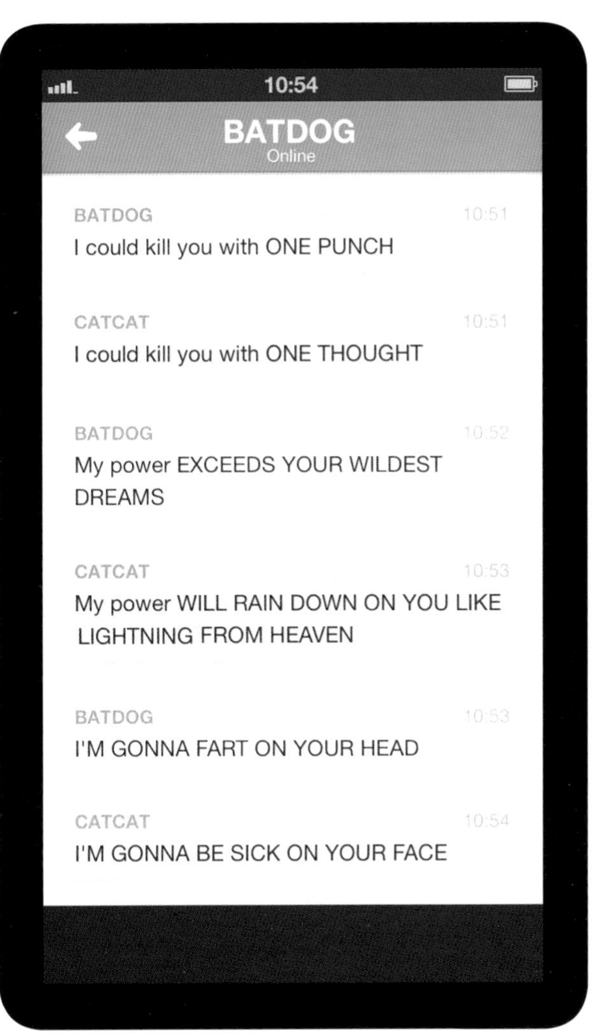
10:54
BATDOG
Online
BATDOG 10:51
I could kill you with ONE PUNCH
CATCAT 10:51
I could kill you with ONE THOUGHT
BATDOG 10:52
My power EXCEEDS YOUR WILDEST DREAMS
CATCAT 10:53
My power WILL RAIN DOWN ON YOU LIKE LIGHTNING FROM HEAVEN
BATDOG 10:53
I'M GONNA FART ON YOUR HEAD
CATCAT 10:54
I'M GONNA BE SICK ON YOUR FACE

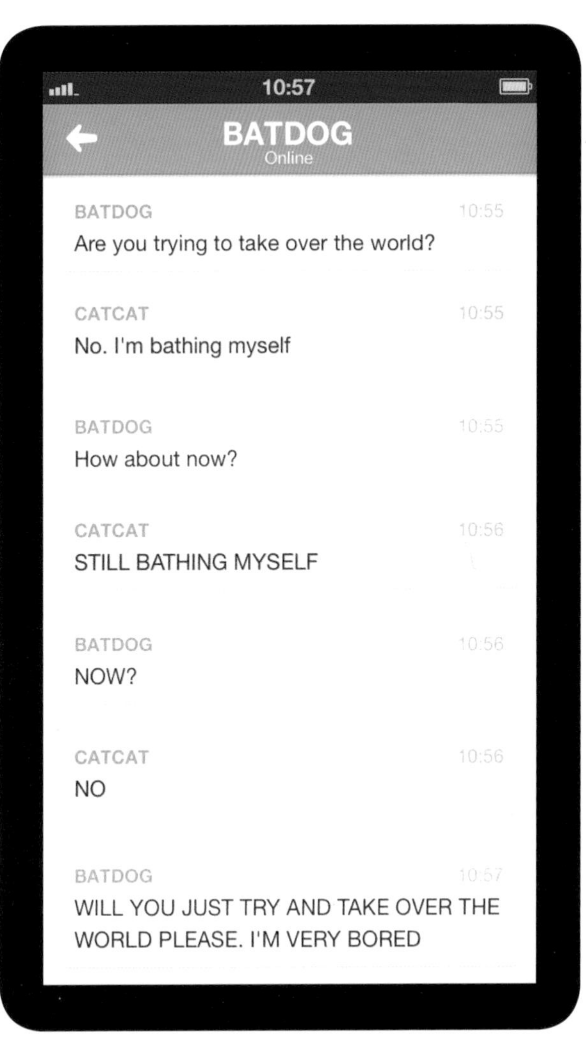
10:57
BATDOG
Online
BATDOG 10:55
Are you trying to take over the world?
CATCAT 10:55
No. I'm bathing myself
BATDOG 10:55
How about now?
CATCAT 10:56
STILL BATHING MYSELF
BATDOG 10:56
NOW?
CATCAT 10:56
NO
BATDOG 10:57
WILL YOU JUST TRY AND TAKE OVER THE WORLD PLEASE. I'M VERY BORED

17:59
Messages
Dog
Edit
I have a new sidekick
Who is it this time?
Picture this...
Jesus Christ
Message
Send

TO DO

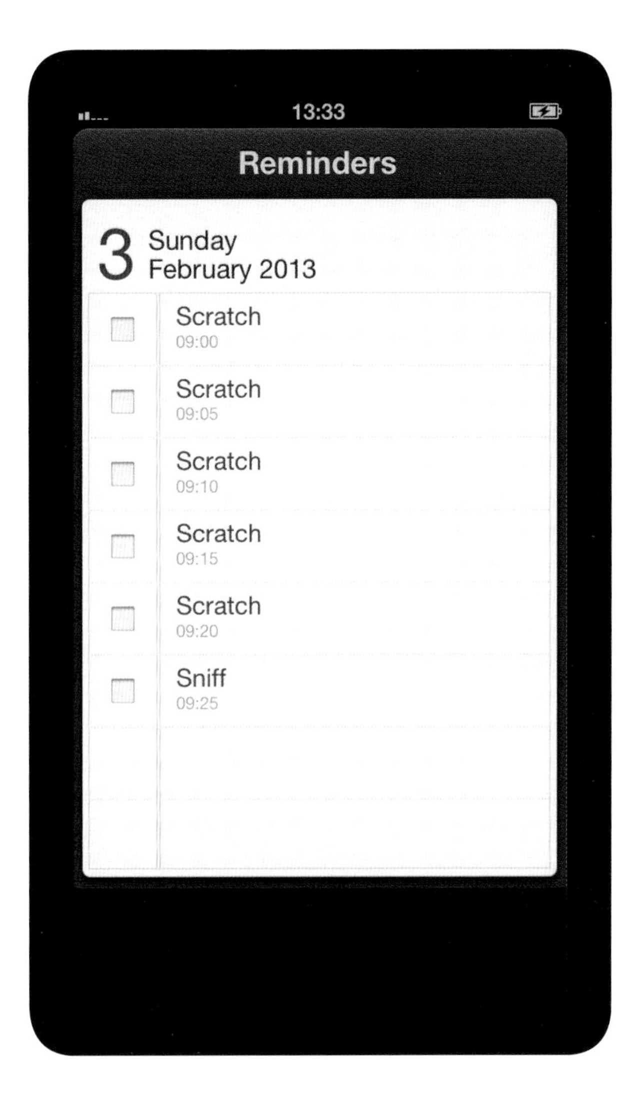
13:33
Reminders
3 Sunday
February 2013
Scratch
09:00
Scratch
09:05
Scratch
09:10
Scratch
09:15
Scratch
09:20
Sniff
09:25

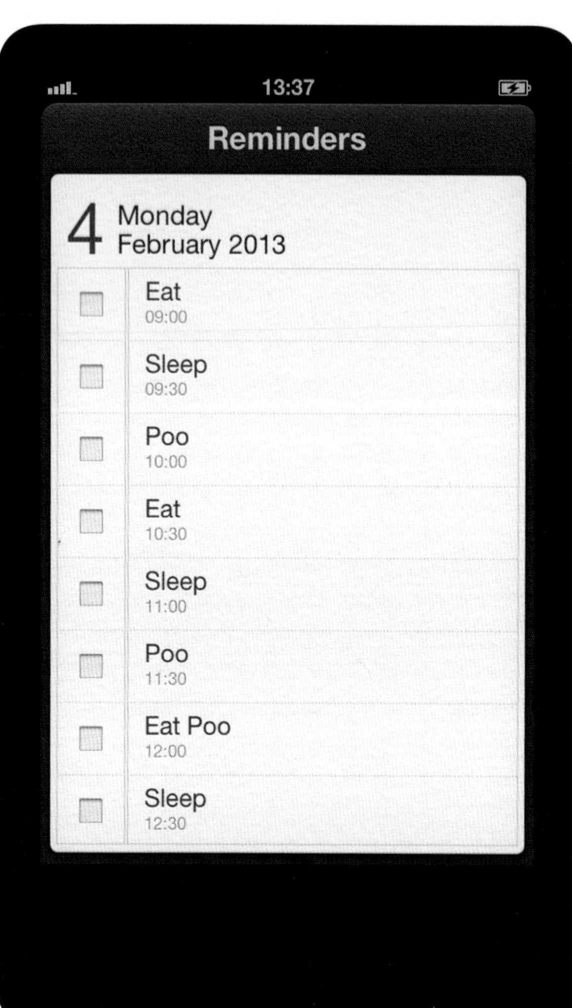
13:37
Reminders
4 Monday
February 2013
Eat
09:00
Sleep
09:30
Poo
10:00
Eat
10:30
Sleep
11:00
Poo
11:30
Eat Poo
12:00
Sleep
12:30

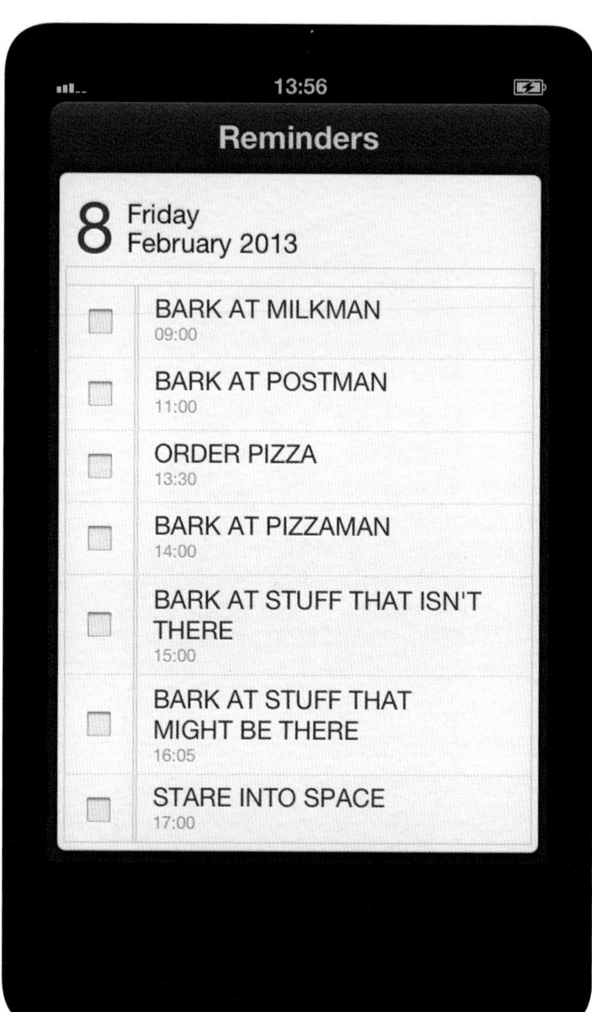
13:56
Reminders
8 Friday
February 2013
BARK AT MILKMAN
09:00
BARK AT POSTMAN
11:00
ORDER PIZZA
13:30
BARK AT PIZZAMAN
14:00
BARK AT STUFF THAT ISN'T THERE
15:00
BARK AT STUFF THAT MIGHT BE THERE
16:05
STARE INTO SPACE
17:00

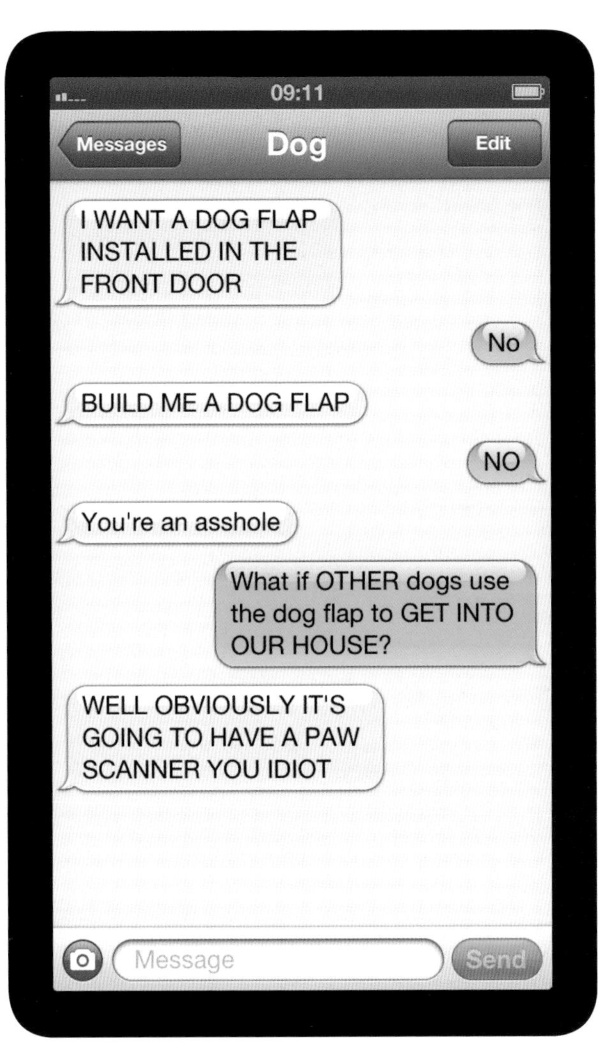
09:11
Messages
Dog
Edit
I WANT A DOG FLAP INSTALLED IN THE FRONT DOOR
No
BUILD ME A DOG FLAP
NO
You're an asshole
What if OTHER dogs use the dog flap to GET INTO OUR HOUSE?
WELL OBVIOUSLY IT'S GOING TO HAVE A PAW SCANNER YOU IDIOT
Message
Send

10:14
Messages
Dog
Edit
Apparently humans can catch ringworm off dogs
I know
Something to think about
Is that a threat?
OF COURSE NOT
I'm just saying, if you're not nice to me from now on I'm going to give you ringworm ON PURPOSE
THAT'S A THREAT
I KNOW. I LIED. I'M EVIL
Message
Send

11:51
Messages
Dog
Edit
OMFG LISTEN TO THIS AWESOME STORY
I'm pretty busy
Earlier a guy walked past the house and I THOUGHT HE WAS YOU
Right
But it WASN'T YOU
Ok
I THOUGHT HE WAS YOU
Yeah
But he WASN'T YOU
Yeah. Got that
THAT'S THE STORY
Message
Send

12:00
Messages
Dog
Edit
Sometimes I try to kill you while you sleep
What?
What?
What?
What?
You just said you TRY TO KILL ME WHILE I SLEEP
No I didn't
I can STILL SEE IT
Sometimes I try to kill you while you sleep
YOU DID IT AGAIN
Did what?
Message
Send

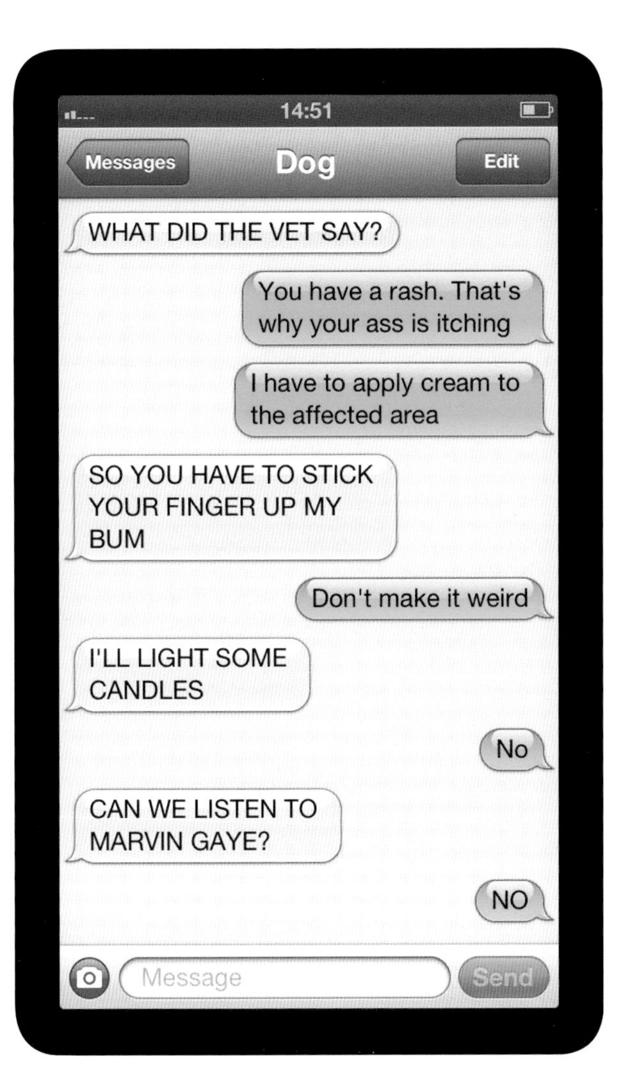
14:51
Messages
Dog
Edit
WHAT DID THE VET SAY?
You have a rash. That's why your ass is itching
I have to apply cream to the affected area
SO YOU HAVE TO STICK YOUR FINGER UP MY BUM
Don't make it weird
I'LL LIGHT SOME CANDLES
No
CAN WE LISTEN TO MARVIN GAYE?
NO
Message
Send

BUM TAB LETS

17:24
Messages
Dog
Edit
IT'S ALMOST HALLOWEEN
We can go Trick or Treating!
YES
You can go as BATDOG
WHY? WILL I NEED TO KICK SOMEONE'S ASS?
OMFG NO. It's just for FUN
BATDOG IS NOT FUN
BATDOG IS A WAY OF LIFE
Message
Send

10:37
Messages
Dog
Edit
YOU SPILLED COFFEE ON THE FLOOR
I'll clean it up when I get back
NO NEED. LICKED IT UP
Caffeine is not for dogs
FEEL ALERT. ENTERING GUARD DOG MODE
GOING TO NEUTRALISE POSTMAN
ABORT
NEGATIVE. DEPLOYING BATDOG BELLY FLOP
Message
Send

19:34
Messages
Dog
Edit
If you do have sex with your girlfriend, don't tell me about it
I wasn't going to
The thought of humans having sex makes me want to cut out my eyes, slice off my ears and then drown in a bath full of my own VOMIT and BLOOD.
Seriously. You guys are HIDEOUSLY VILE
No offence
How could I POSSIBLY find that offensive?
Message
Send

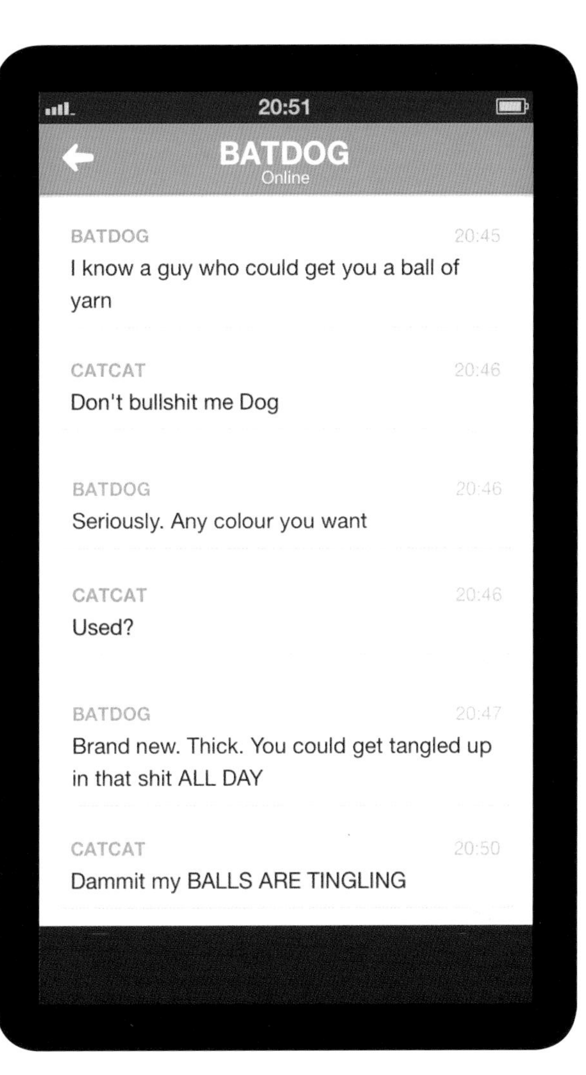
20:51
BATDOG
Online
BATDOG 20:45
I know a guy who could get you a ball of yarn
CATCAT 20:46
Don't bullshit me Dog
BATDOG 20:46
Seriously. Any colour you want
CATCAT 20:46
Used?
BATDOG 20:47
Brand new. Thick. You could get tangled up in that shit ALL DAY
CATCAT 20:50
Dammit my BALLS ARE TINGLING

02:53
Messages
Dog
Edit
OMFG I'M PLAYING IN THE SNOW
That's nice
I'M SO FLIPPIN' HAPPY
Good
I made you a SLUSH PUPPY
No thanks
I made you a SLUSH PUPPY because I LOVE YOU. If you don't eat it our friendship is OVER
What flavour is it?
YELLOW
Message
Send

19:31
Messages
Dog
Edit
You know what I LOVE about the snow?
What?
You can't see my poo until it's TOO LATE
THE GARDEN'S LIKE A MINEFIELD
AAAAAHAHAHAHAHAHA HAHAHAHAHAHAHAHAH AHAHAHAHAHAHAHAHA
Message
Send

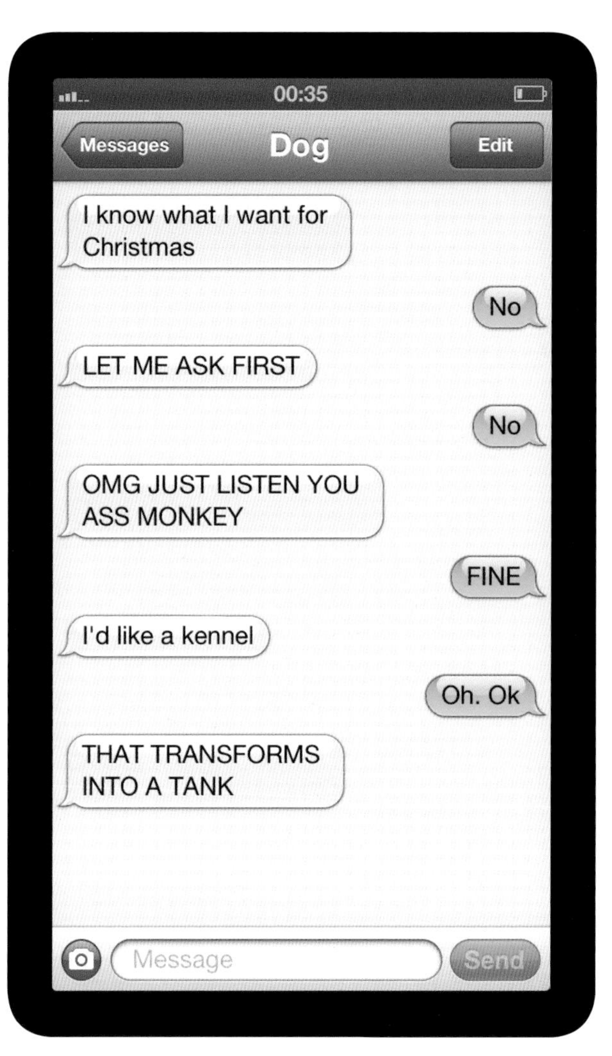
00:35
Messages
Dog
Edit
I know what I want for Christmas
No
LET ME ASK FIRST
No
OMG JUST LISTEN YOU ASS MONKEY
FINE
I'd like a kennel
Oh. Ok
THAT TRANSFORMS INTO A TANK
Message
Send

08:51
Messages
Dog
Edit
Where am I?
IN THE PARK
Where are you?
IN THE PARK
What happened?
I let you off your leash and you took off like a FAT FURRY MISSILE
What were you THINKING?
AWESOME AWESOME AWESOME AWESOME AWESOME AWESOME AWESOME AWESOME AWESOME AWESOME AWESOME AWESOME
Message
Send

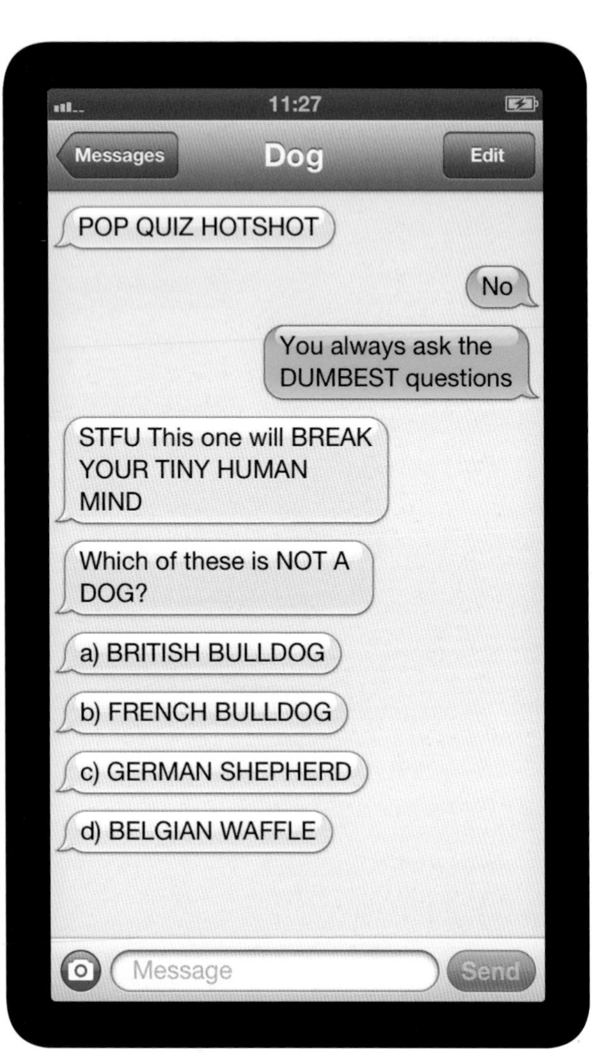
11:27
Messages
Dog
Edit
POP QUIZ HOTSHOT
No
You always ask the DUMBEST questions
STFU This one will BREAK YOUR TINY HUMAN MIND
Which of these is NOT A DOG?
a) BRITISH BULLDOG
b) FRENCH BULLDOG
c) GERMAN SHEPHERD
d) BELGIAN WAFFLE
Message
Send

15:47
Messages
Dog
Edit
TODAY I'VE DONE NOTHING BUT SLEEP AND GET FATTER
I'll take you to the park when I get back
WHAT FOR?
Exercise
I'M BUSY
Doing what?
SLEEPING AND GETTING FATTER
Message
Send

13:50
Messages
Dog
Edit
HOW LONG DID IT TAKE YOU TO PUT UP THE CHRISTMAS TREE?
Two hours
I PULLED IT DOWN IN 15 SECONDS
YOU'VE LET JESUS DOWN
Message
Send

23:07
Messages
Dog
Edit
HUMANS ARE SINGING AT FRONT DOOR
That's what people do at Christmas
WHY?
To spread goodwill and cheer!
WHY ARE YOU UPSTAIRS WITH THE DOOR CLOSED?
JUST SCARE THEM OFF OK?
Message
Send

17:06
Messages
Dog
Edit
Does your new 'girlfriend' have a dog?
Stop putting girlfriend in air quotes. She has a cat
OMFG
What?
Nothing
WHAT?
NOTHING. Your 'girlfriend' is obviously IN LEAGUE WITH THE DEVIL
It's FINE
Message
Send

17:42
Messages
Dog
Edit
DEAR SANTA. Here is my Christmas list. Please be aware that I AM BATDOG and if I don't get EVERYTHING on this list I will HUNT YOU DOWN AND KILL YOU LIKE A MOOSE
I WOULD LIKE:
1. A Rocket Launcher
2. Epic Rubber Nipples
3. Dog Jeans (really tight)
4. Bum sex with Lassie
5. My testicles back
FYI, My testicles were MASSIVE
Message
Send

09:18
Messages
Dog
Edit
DID YOU GET ME A BALL FOR CHRISTMAS?
I'm not telling you
DID YOU GET ME A BALL FOR CHRISTMAS?
I'm not telling you
DID YOU GET ME A BALL FOR CHRISTMAS?
I'M NOT TELLING YOU
DID YOU GET ME A BALL FOR CHRISTMAS?
YES
OMFG THANKS FOR RUINING THE SURPRISE
Message
Send

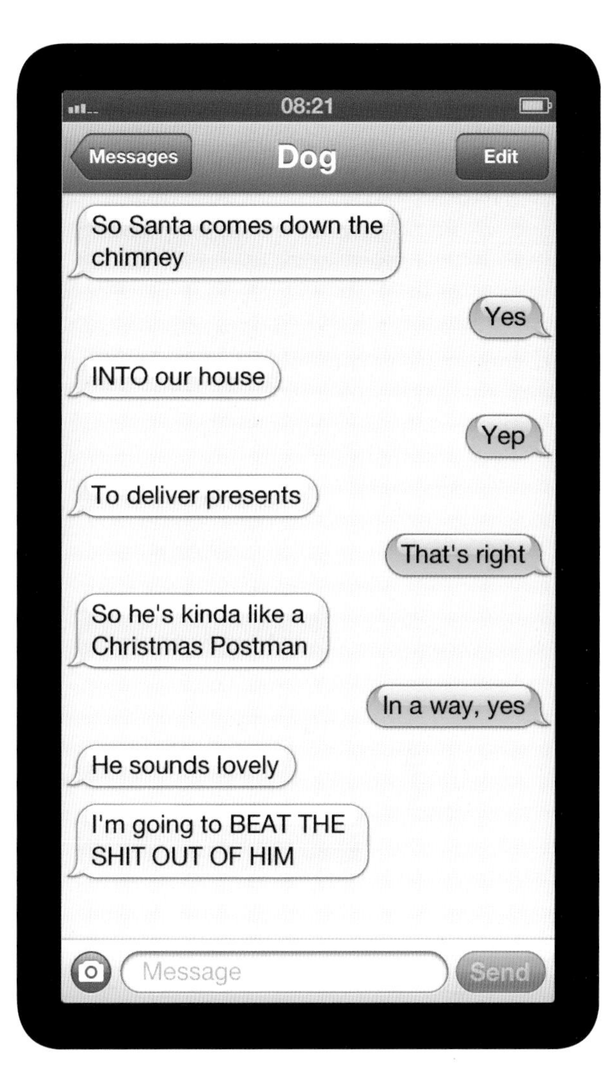
08:21
Messages
Dog
Edit
So Santa comes down the chimney
Yes
INTO our house
Yep
To deliver presents
That's right
So he's kinda like a Christmas Postman
In a way, yes
He sounds lovely
I'm going to BEAT THE SHIT OUT OF HIM
Message
Send

hohoho

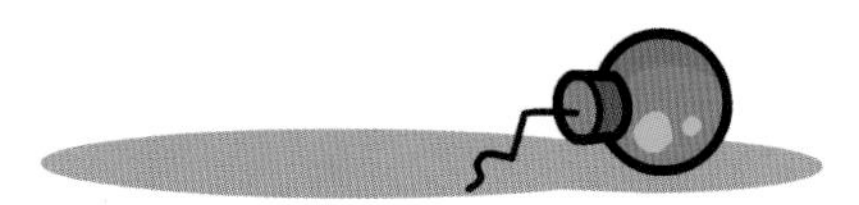

08:14
Messages
Dog
Edit
MERRY CHRISTMAS HUMAN. HAPPY NEW YEAR
Thanks. What's your New Year's Resolution?
WHAT'S A NEW YEAR'S RESOLUTION?
Something you're going to change in the New Year in order to make your life better
I'M ALREADY A DOG
LIFE DOESN'T GET ANY BETTER THAN THAT
Message
Send

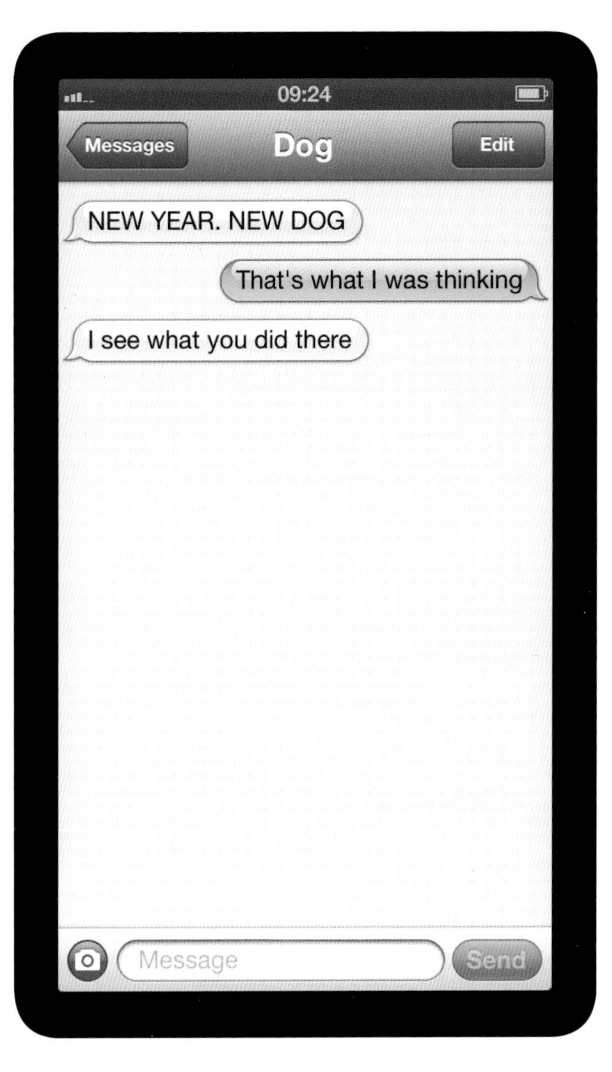
09:24
Messages
Dog
Edit
NEW YEAR. NEW DOG
That's what I was thinking
I see what you did there
Message
Send

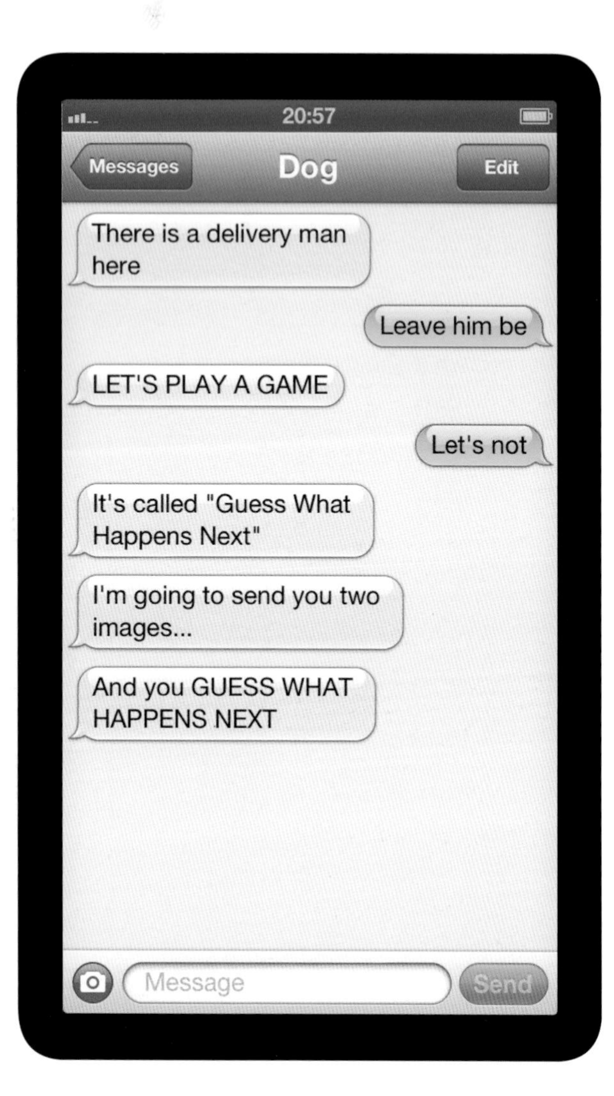
20:57
Messages
Dog
Edit
There is a delivery man here
Leave him be
LET'S PLAY A GAME
Let's not
It's called "Guess What Happens Next"
I'm going to send you two images...
And you GUESS WHAT HAPPENS NEXT
Message
Send

11:18
Messages
Dog
Edit
He's dead
Message
Send

10:49
Messages
Dog
Edit
IT'S RAINING CATS AND DOGS
It's not raining
IT'S RAINING CATS
It's NOT raining
IT'S RAINING A CAT
I threw a cat off the roof
OMFG
Message
Send

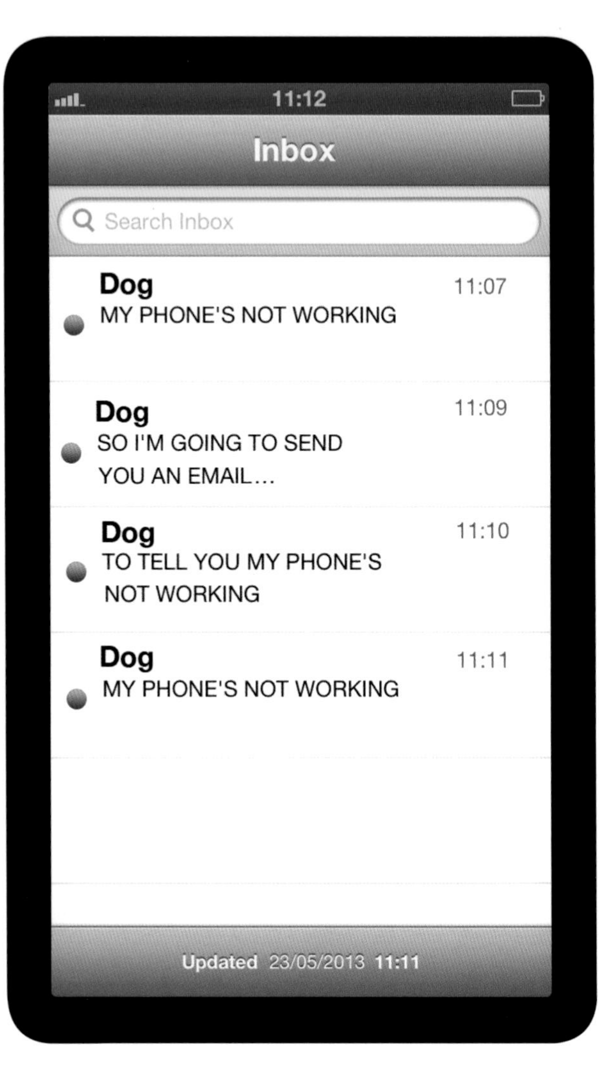
11:12
Inbox
Search Inbox
Dog
11:07
MY PHONE'S NOT WORKING
Dog
11:09
SO I'M GOING TO SEND YOU AN EMAIL…
Dog
11:10
TO TELL YOU MY PHONE'S NOT WORKING
Dog
11:11
MY PHONE'S NOT WORKING
Updated 23/05/2013 11:11

16:59
Messages
Dog
Edit
I love that cute thing your girlfriend does
What cute thing?
That cute thing
WHAT cute thing?
That cute thing where she goes home forever and STOPS RUINING OUR LIVES
Message
Send

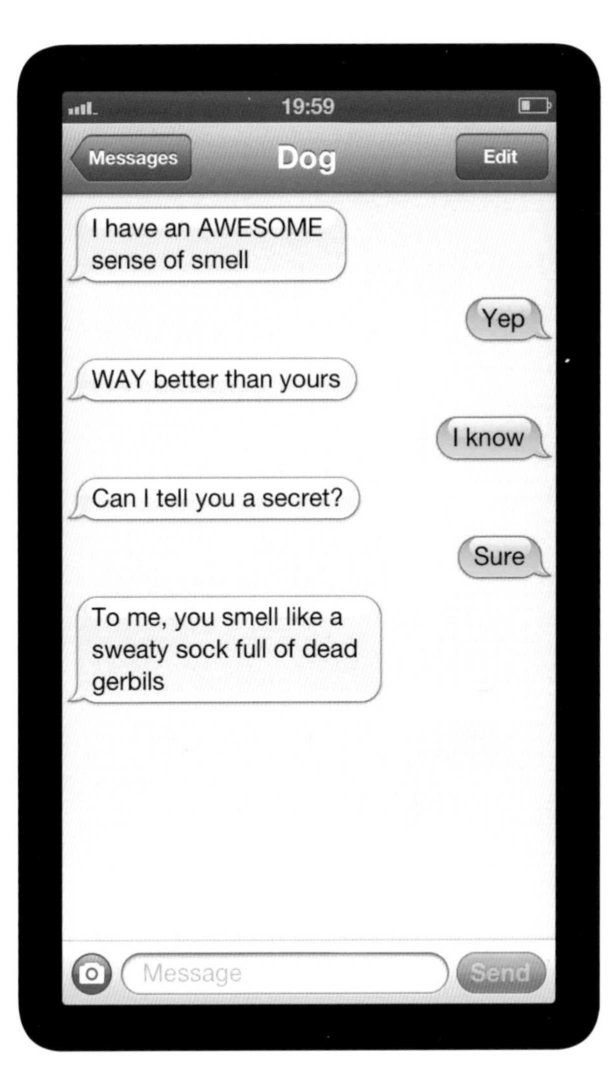
19:59
Messages
Dog
Edit
I have an AWESOME sense of smell
Yep
WAY better than yours
I know
Can I tell you a secret?
Sure
To me, you smell like a sweaty sock full of dead gerbils
Message
Send

00:39
Messages
Dog
Edit
Can we try switching roles? I'll be the owner, you be the Dog
GREAT IDEA
LOOK AT ME DOING ANNOYING SHIT FOR SOME REASON. IS THAT FOR ME? CAN I HAVE THAT? DOOR! DOOR! DOOR! RUB ME RUB ME RUB ME RUB ME! ME ME ME ME! I'M SO EXCITED THIS IS THE BEST DAY EVER OF ALL TIME
OOH I'M SO WORRIED ABOUT BILLS AND HEY LET'S START A WAR AND KILL SOME POLAR BEARS AND HIT SEALS TILL THEY DIE! I'M SUCH A STUPID FACED TWONK
Message
Send

18:28
Messages
Dog
Edit
We just kicked the crap out of a bunch of squirrels
STOP FIGHTING SQUIRRELS FFS
THEY AMBUSHED US
Who are you with?
HAYLO HOOMAN
Jesus Christ
EYE HEADBATTED A SQUARRAL
Message
Send

07:48
Messages
Dog
Edit
DO YOU MESS WITH MY FACE WHILE I'M ASLEEP?
No
DO YOU MESS WITH MY FACE WHILE I'M ASLEEP?
No
DO YOU MESS WITH MY FACE WHILE I'M ASLEEP?
Message
Send

07:48
427 of 428

12:25
Messages (2)
Dog
Edit
Did you call me? I'm busy
I'M AN UNCLE!
OMG THAT'S AMAZING
I KNOW!
WHAT DOES THAT MAKE ME?
A DOG
OH
I CAN'T WAIT TO PLAY WITH THE BABY
You're not going anywhere near the baby
I HATE THIS KID ALREADY
Message
Send

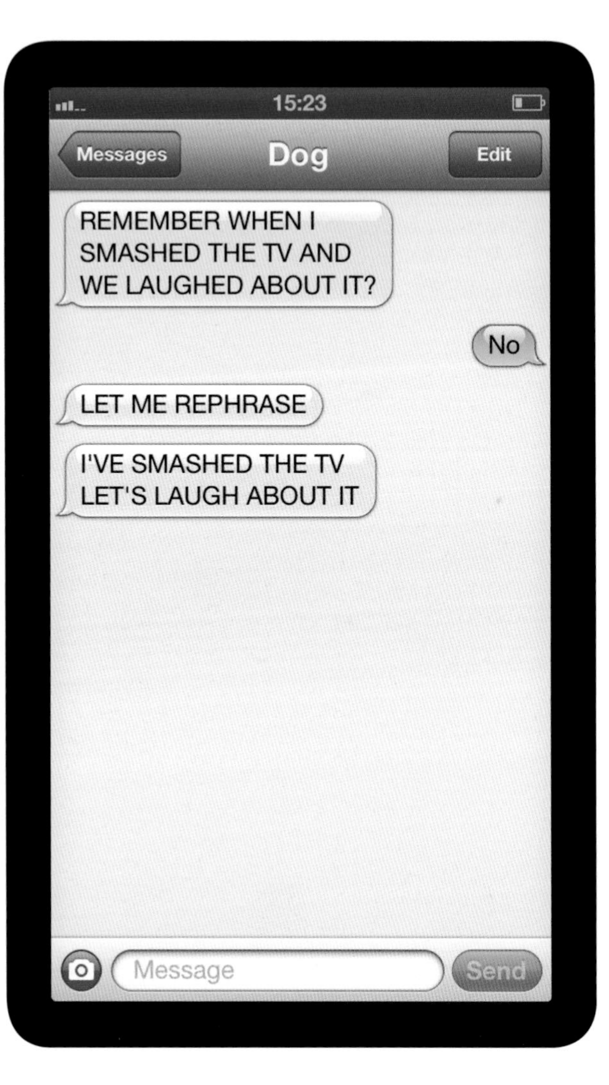
15:23
Messages
Dog
Edit
REMEMBER WHEN I SMASHED THE TV AND WE LAUGHED ABOUT IT?
No
LET ME REPHRASE
I'VE SMASHED THE TV LET'S LAUGH ABOUT IT
Message
Send

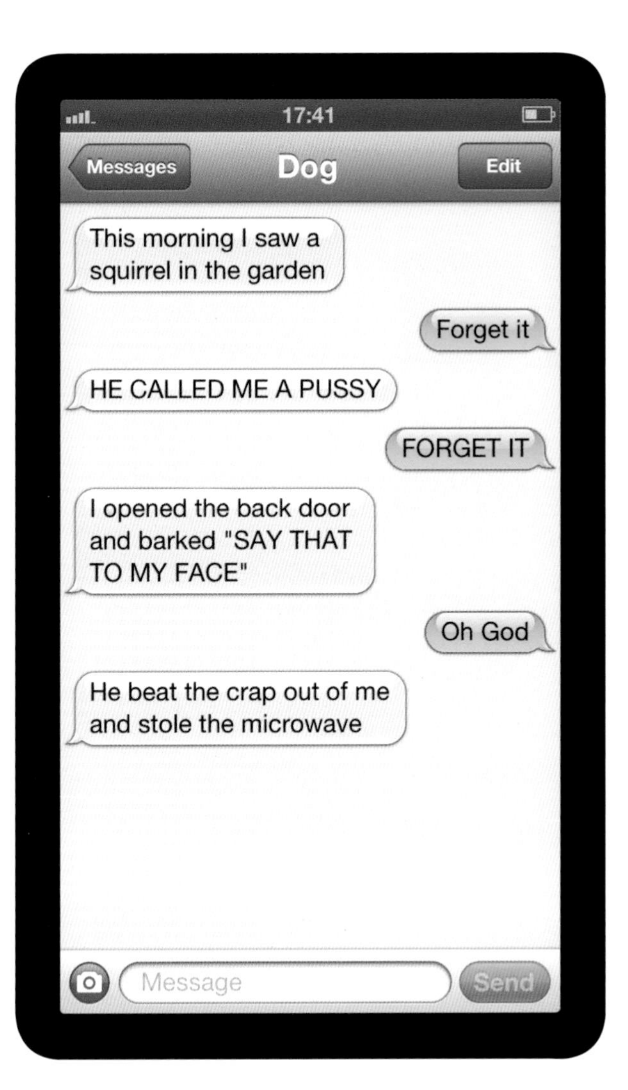
17:41
Messages
Dog
Edit
This morning I saw a squirrel in the garden
Forget it
HE CALLED ME A PUSSY
FORGET IT
I opened the back door and barked "SAY THAT TO MY FACE"
Oh God
He beat the crap out of me and stole the microwave
Message
Send

18:11
Messages
Dog
Edit
So did you have sex with your girlfriend?
Maaaybe
Was it fun? Did you ENJOY IT?
Well :) You know how it is
No I don't because SOMEBODY CHOPPED MY TESTICLES OFF AND SLAM DUNKED THEM INTO A WASTE PAPER BASKET
For the LAST TIME. VETS DON'T SLAM DUNK DOG TESTICLES
OMFG STOP LYING TO ME ASSHOLE
Message
Send

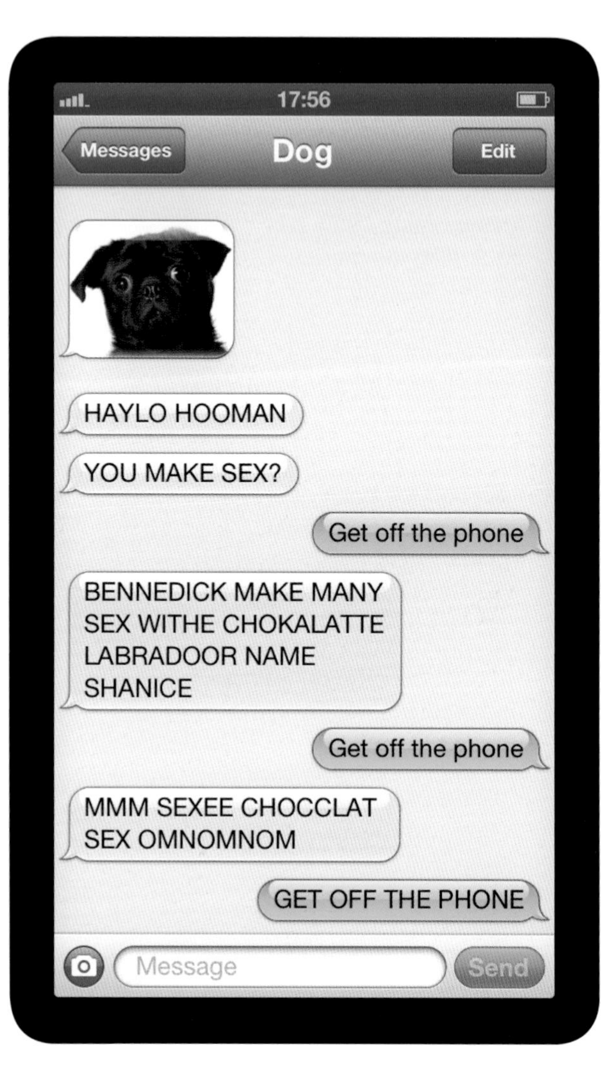
17:56
Messages
Dog
Edit
HAYLO HOOMAN
YOU MAKE SEX?
Get off the phone
BENNEDICK MAKE MANY SEX WITHE CHOKALATTE LABRADOOR NAME SHANICE
Get off the phone
MMM SEXEE CHOCCLAT SEX OMNOMNOM
GET OFF THE PHONE
Message
Send

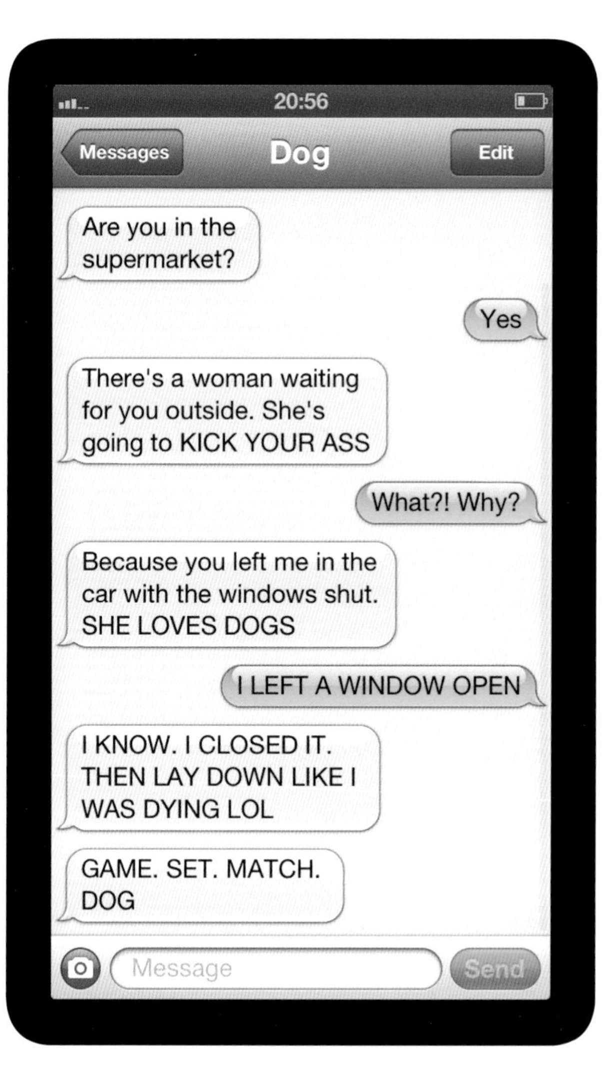
20:56
Messages
Dog
Edit
Are you in the supermarket?
Yes
There's a woman waiting for you outside. She's going to KICK YOUR ASS
What?! Why?
Because you left me in the car with the windows shut. SHE LOVES DOGS
I LEFT A WINDOW OPEN
I KNOW. I CLOSED IT. THEN LAY DOWN LIKE I WAS DYING LOL
GAME. SET. MATCH. DOG
Message
Send

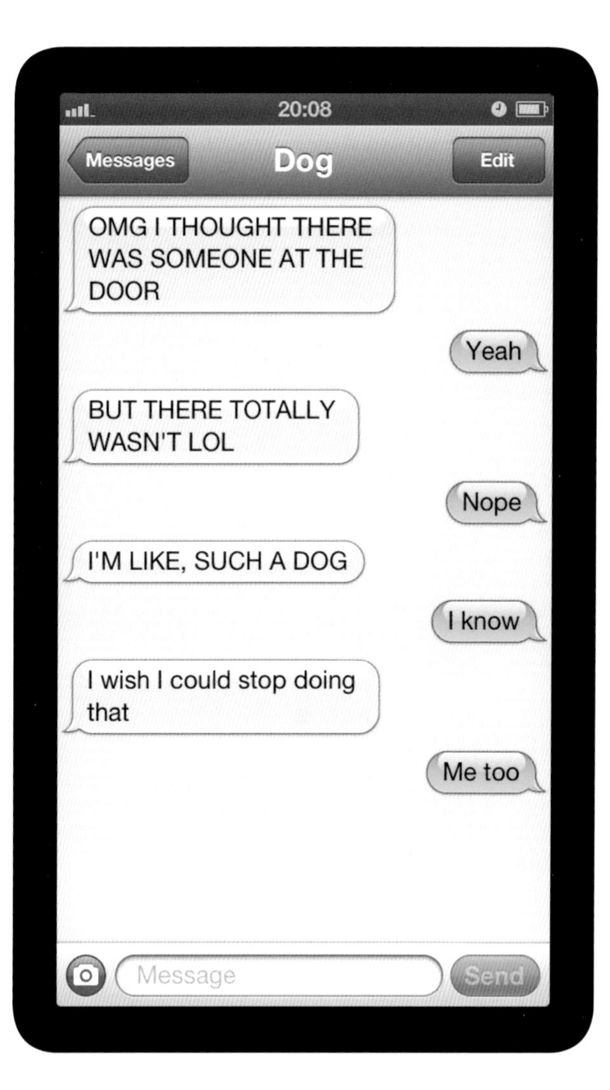
20:08
Messages
Dog
Edit
OMG I THOUGHT THERE WAS SOMEONE AT THE DOOR
Yeah
BUT THERE TOTALLY WASN'T LOL
Nope
I'M LIKE, SUCH A DOG
I know
I wish I could stop doing that
Me too
Message
Send

12:29
Messages
Dog
Edit
I'M SO BORED I COULD KILL MYSELF
I'll be back soon
Good
I'll kill you instead
Message
Send

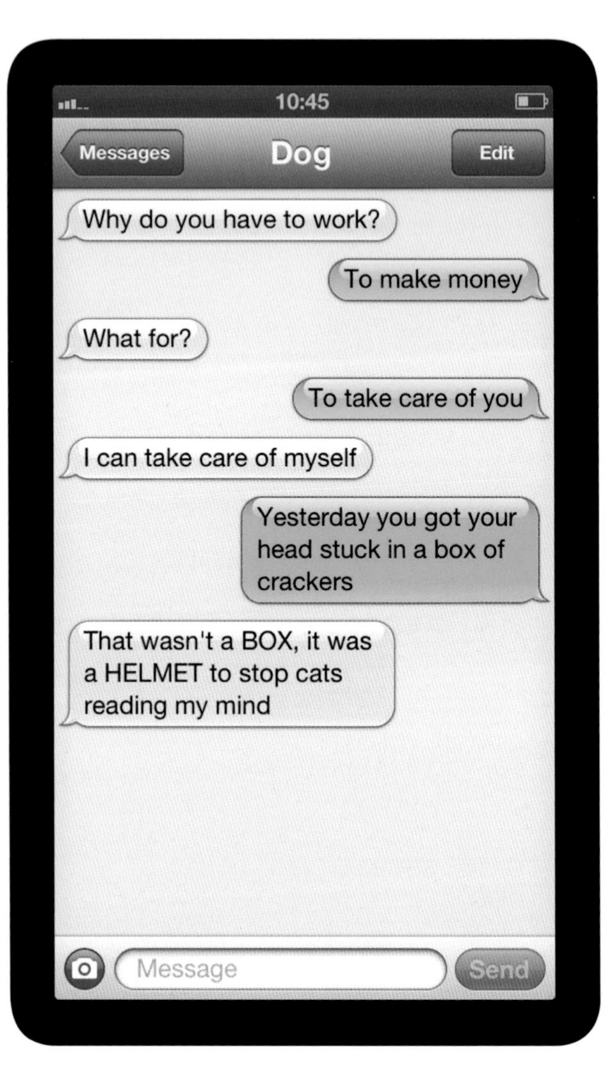
10:45
Messages
Dog
Edit
Why do you have to work?
To make money
What for?
To take care of you
I can take care of myself
Yesterday you got your head stuck in a box of crackers
That wasn't a BOX, it was a HELMET to stop cats reading my mind
Message
Send

07:41
Messages
Dog
Edit
I see you've put a new sign on the door
Yep
Now people are going to think I'm an ASSHOLE
Aww. Why would they think that?
Message
Send

18:51
514 of 514
BEWARE OF DOG
HE'S AN ASSHOLE

16:51
Messages
Dog
Edit
Would you say I'm the BEST dog on the planet?
Yes
Would you say I'm the best human?
Definitely not
Message
Send

12:38
Messages
Dog
Edit
I'M SO EXCITED
Why?
I CAN'T REMEMBER
So why are you still excited?
NOW I'M EXCITED ABOUT BEING EXCITED
HOW CAN YOU BE EXCITED ABOUT BEING EXCITED?
BECAUSE IT'S EXCITING
NOW I'M EXCITED
LET'S GO TO VEGAS
FUCK YEAHHHHHHHH
Message
Send

17:34
Messages
Dog
Edit
Why do humans have such HUGE FEET and such TINY HEADS?
Jesus Christ. How many times? It's PERSPECTIVE. It's because you're always LOOKING UP AT US
Whatever BEAN HEAD
Message
Send

21:58
Messages
Dog
Edit
Your girlfriend called me her BFF. What does that mean?
'Best Friend Forever'
I just threw up in my mouth
I'm going to pretend it means 'BATDOG'S FREAKIN' FUCKAWESOME'
I think 'FUCKAWESOME' is two words
DON'T QUESTION MY FUCKAWESOMENESS
Message
Send

17:19
Messages
Dog
Edit
You need some new pillows
I have plenty of pillows
You HAD plenty of pillows
Message
Send

22:01
Messages
Dog
Edit
DID YOU PUT A NEW PLANT POT IN THE GARDEN?
Yes
THAT'S NOT GOOD. DEFINITELY NOT GOOD. GONNA BARK. GONNA BARK FOR SIX HOURS. DEFINITELY SIX HOURS
Jeez. Alright Rainman
Message
Send

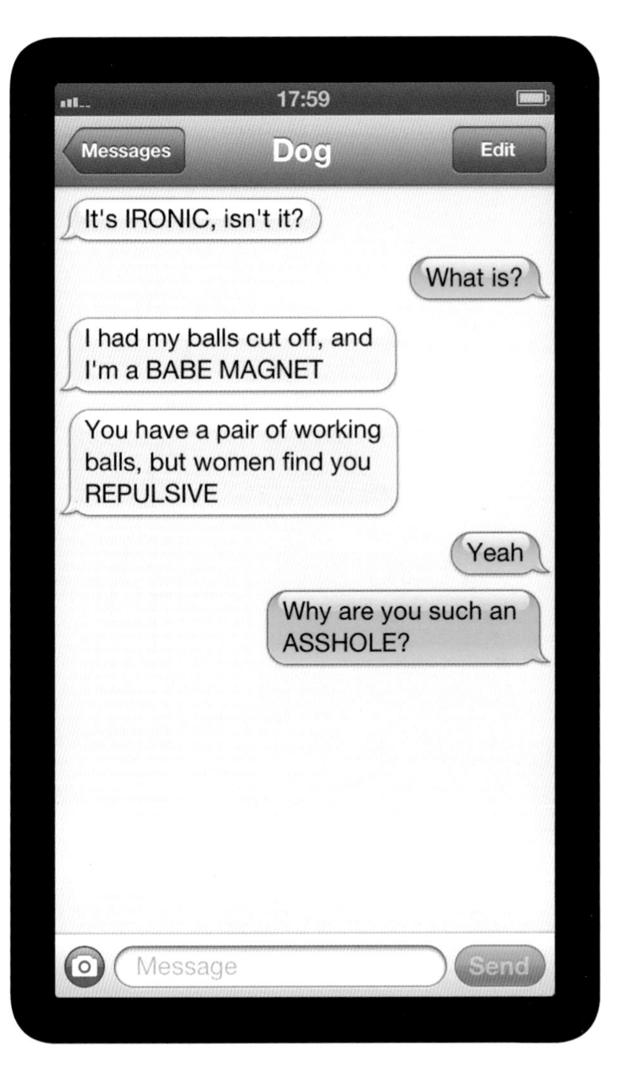
17:59
Messages
Dog
Edit
It's IRONIC, isn't it?
What is?
I had my balls cut off, and I'm a BABE MAGNET
You have a pair of working balls, but women find you REPULSIVE
Yeah
Why are you such an ASSHOLE?
Message
Send

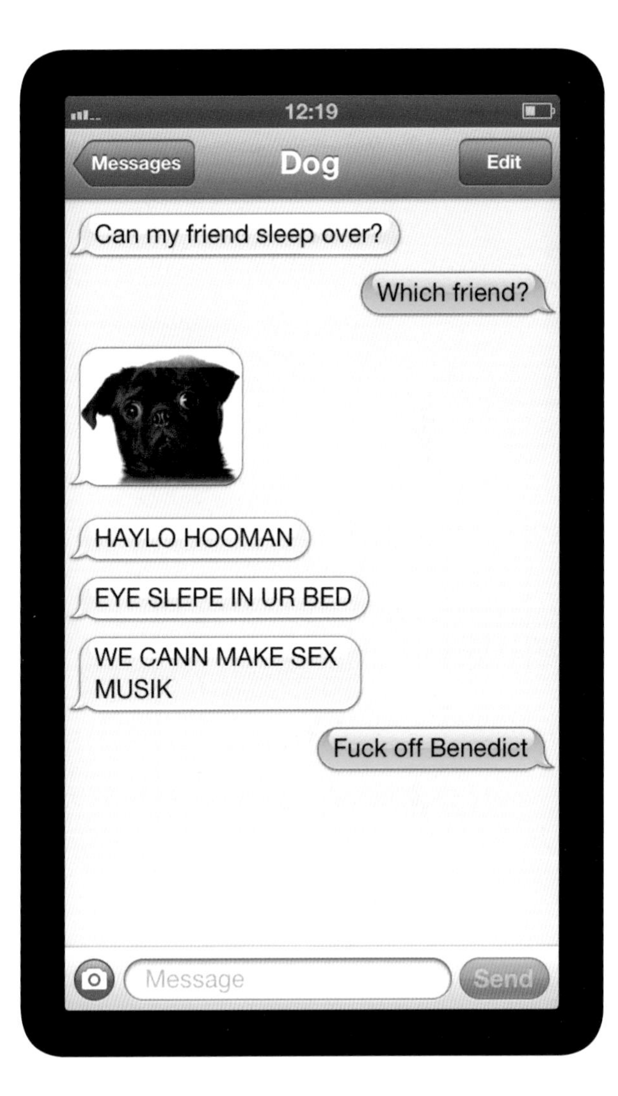
12:19
Messages
Dog
Edit
Can my friend sleep over?
Which friend?
HAYLO HOOMAN
EYE SLEPE IN UR BED
WE CANN MAKE SEX MUSIK
Fuck off Benedict
Message
Send

18:17
Messages
Dog
Edit
HOW LONG DO I HAVE TO WEAR THIS CONE?
Until your stitches come out
I LOOK RIDICULOUS
So STOP FIGHTING SQUIRRELS
I KEEP BANGING INTO WALLS
JUST SIT DOWN
WHEN I SIT DOWN I LOOK LIKE A DESK LAMP
Message
Send

21:43
Messages
Dog
Edit
YOU CAN'T LEAVE A PEDIGREE BULLDOG IN A KENNEL NUMBNUTS
And yet, I have
TO THE MONGRELS HERE I'M LIKE A SUPERHOT PIECE OF DOG CHOCOLATE
You're BATDOG
ARE YOU KIDDING? I CAN'T PUT MY CAPE ON. THAT'D BE LIKE A SEXY OVERLOAD
Message
Send

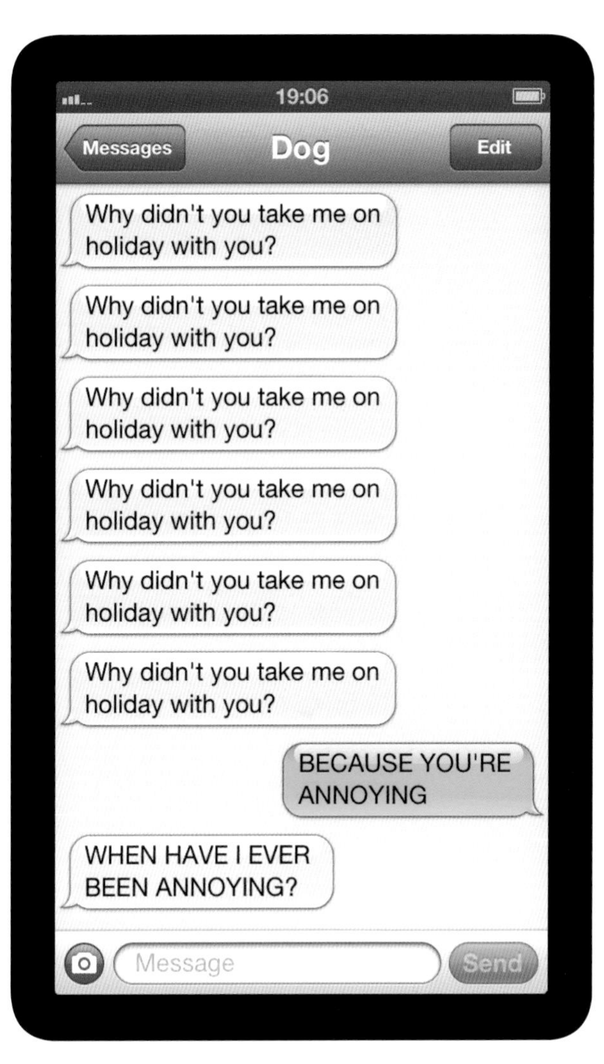
19:06
Messages
Dog
Edit
Why didn't you take me on holiday with you?
Why didn't you take me on holiday with you?
Why didn't you take me on holiday with you?
Why didn't you take me on holiday with you?
Why didn't you take me on holiday with you?
Why didn't you take me on holiday with you?
BECAUSE YOU'RE ANNOYING
WHEN HAVE I EVER BEEN ANNOYING?
Message
Send

11:45
Messages
Dog
Edit
Are you enjoying your holiday?
Yes. How's the kennel?
HELL ON EARTH. I'M BEING SEXUALISED BY A GANG OF PUGS AND THE FOOD MAKES ME WISH I WAS DEAD
I hope you're having a lovely time x
Message
Send

19:11
Messages
Dog
Edit
Why didn't you take me on holiday with you?
There are NO DOGS allowed in the hotel
FINE. Maybe I'LL go on holiday to a hotel that doesn't allow HUMANS
Right. What's that hotel called again?
It's called the FUCK OFF TWO LEGS INN
Catchy
Message
Send

08:58
Messages
Dog
Edit
Ted the Terrier just said he doesn't think I can beat up a swan
I don't care
I need you to find me a swan so I can beat it up
Swans are protected by the Queen
THEN I'LL BEAT HER UP TOO
Message
Send

09:05
Messages
Dog
Edit
HEAD TRAPPED IN FENCE
Jesus. Stay calm
NEGATIVE. GOING APE SHIT
STAY CALM
OH GOD. OH GOD
THERE'S A SQUIRREL
Ignore him
HE'S RUBBING HIS TESTICLES IN MY FACE
It's actually quite pleasant
OMFG I'M SQUIRREL GAY
Message
Send

23:21
Messages
Dog
Edit
Tell me a joke
Nope
C'MON. I GET human jokes now
"My Dog's got no nose"
"How does he smell?"
"Awful"
THANKS. NOW I HAVE A BODY ODOUR COMPLEX
Message
Send

22:49
Messages
Dog
Edit
I JUST READ THAT YOU SENT A DOG INTO SPACE AND IT DIED
Not me personally
DO YOU THINK IT'S OK TO SEND A DOG INTO SPACE TO DIE?
Depends which Dog
IF YOU SENT ME UP THERE I'D GET JESUS TO COME DOWN AND KICK YOUR HEAD IN
Message
Send

16:55
Messages
Dog
Edit
I've finally come to terms with you having a girlfriend
Thank you
I know. I'm a wonderful friend
You are :)
I'll let you be Best Dog at my wedding
IF YOU MARRY HER I'LL KILL MYSELF
Message
Send

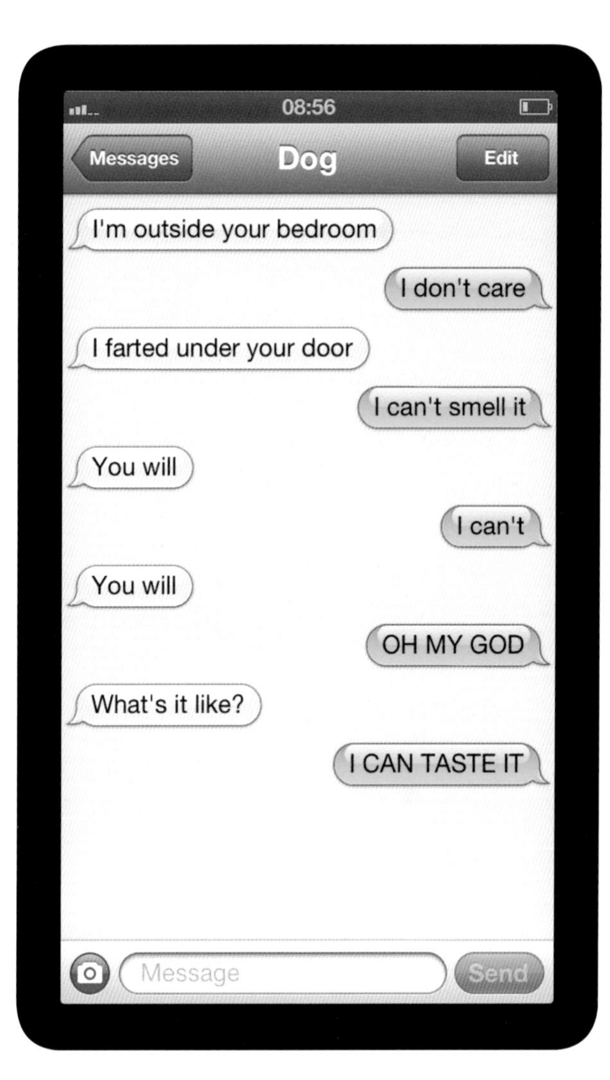
08:56
Messages
Dog
Edit
I'm outside your bedroom
I don't care
I farted under your door
I can't smell it
You will
I can't
You will
OH MY GOD
What's it like?
I CAN TASTE IT
Message
Send

19:24
Messages
Dog
Edit
WHERE DO WE KEEP THE GUNS?
Under the sink
I can't find them
WE DON'T HAVE ANY GUNS
WHY WOULD YOU JOKE ABOUT THAT? NOW WE'RE GOING TO DIE
How?
SQUIRREL MAFIA
Message
Send

19:39
Messages
Dog
Edit
I love you SO MUCH. Sometimes I love you SO MUCH I CAN'T BREATHE
That's sweet
Sometimes I love you so much I touch myself
That's weird
Message
Send

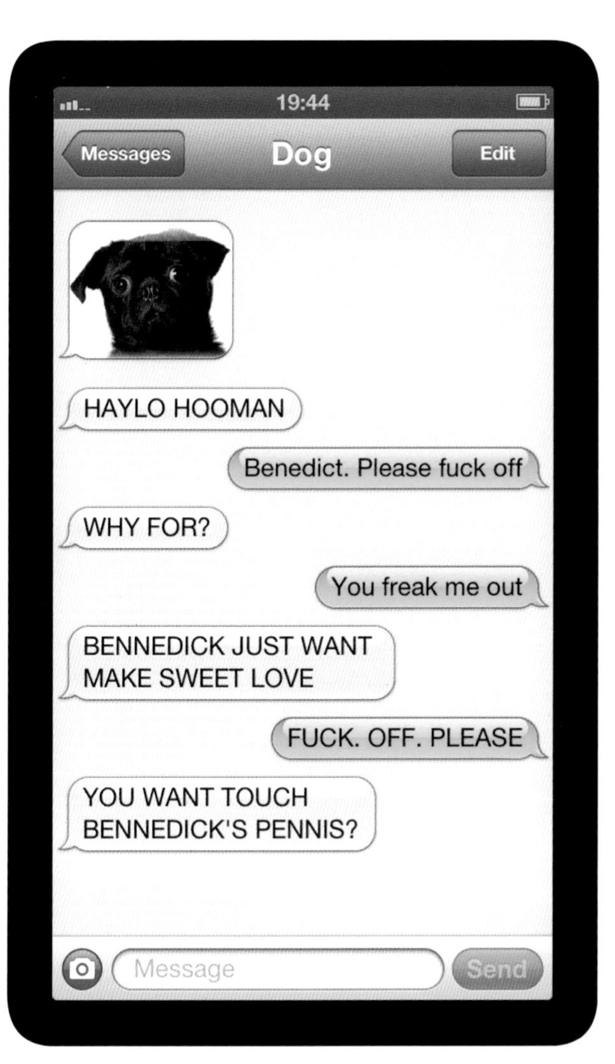
19:44
Messages
Dog
Edit
HAYLO HOOMAN
Benedict. Please fuck off
WHY FOR?
You freak me out
BENNEDICK JUST WANT MAKE SWEET LOVE
FUCK. OFF. PLEASE
YOU WANT TOUCH BENNEDICK'S PENNIS?
Message
Send

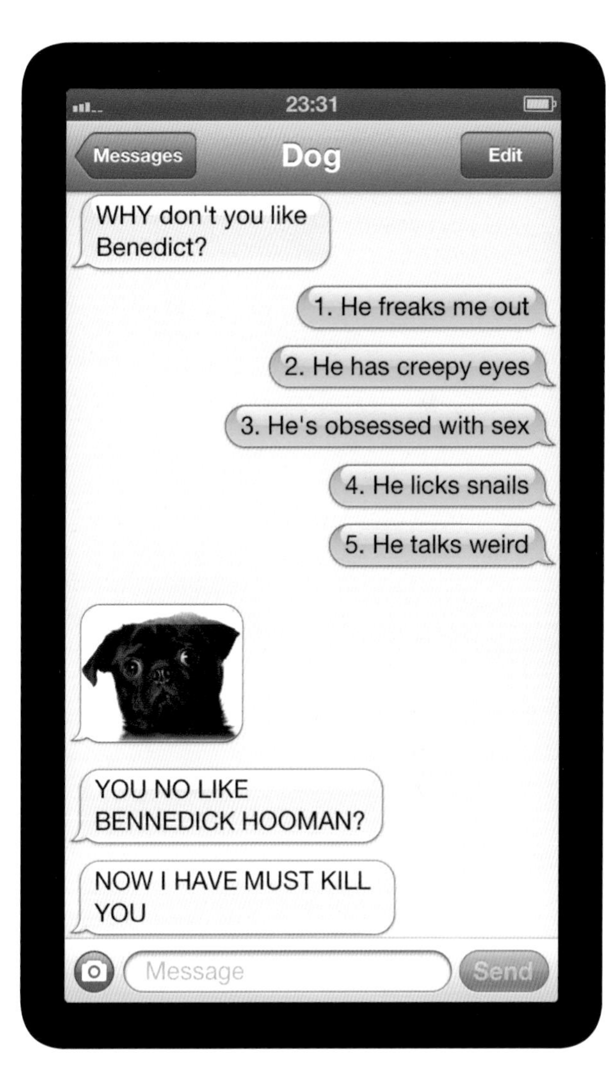
23:31
Messages
Dog
Edit
WHY don't you like Benedict?
1. He freaks me out
2. He has creepy eyes
3. He's obsessed with sex
4. He licks snails
5. He talks weird
YOU NO LIKE BENNEDICK HOOMAN?
NOW I HAVE MUST KILL YOU
Message
Send

20:15
Messages
Dog
Edit
Why am I called a 'Bulldog'?
It's short for BULLSHIT DOG
OMFG I'M FULL OF IT
Yeah you are
Message
Send

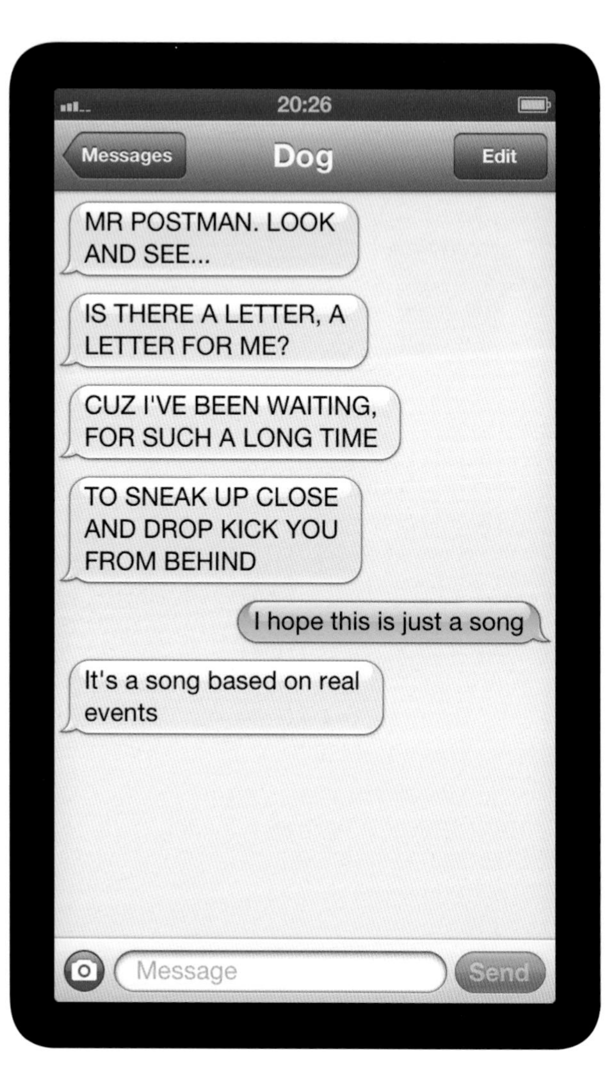
20:26
Messages
Dog
Edit
MR POSTMAN. LOOK AND SEE...
IS THERE A LETTER, A LETTER FOR ME?
CUZ I'VE BEEN WAITING, FOR SUCH A LONG TIME
TO SNEAK UP CLOSE AND DROP KICK YOU FROM BEHIND
I hope this is just a song
It's a song based on real events
Message
Send

18:19
Messages
Dog
Edit
Me and CATCAT finally found something we AGREE on
Thank God. My life is now complete
Message
Send

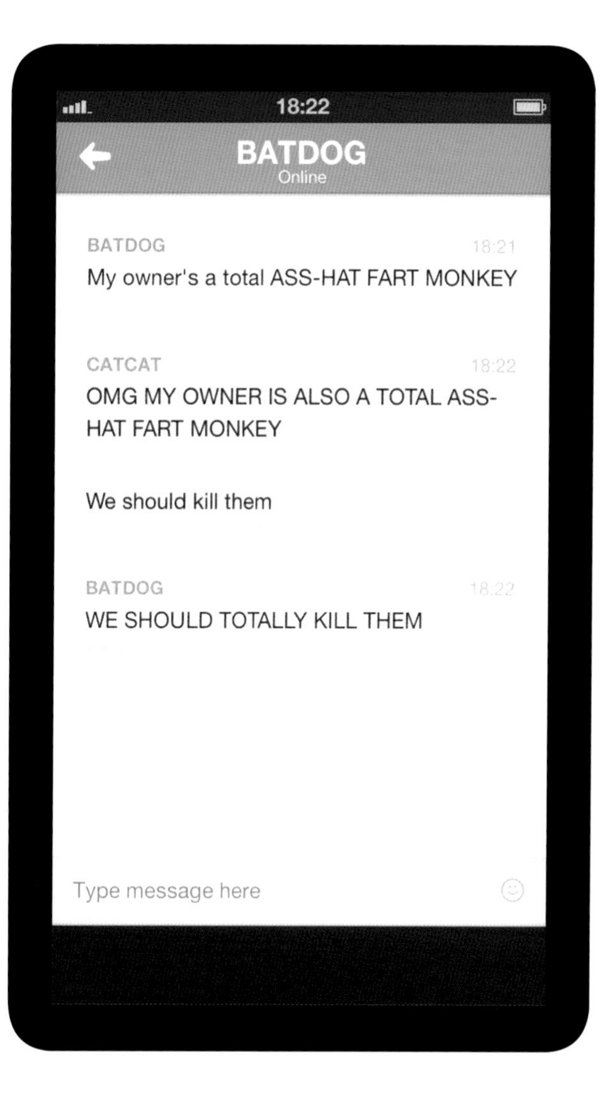
18:22
BATDOG
Online
BATDOG
18:21
My owner's a total ASS-HAT FART MONKEY
CATCAT
18:22
OMG MY OWNER IS ALSO A TOTAL ASS-HAT FART MONKEY
We should kill them
BATDOG
18:22
WE SHOULD TOTALLY KILL THEM
Type message here

22:06
Messages
Dog
Edit
Want to know a DOG SECRET?
Sure
Dogs aren't really scared of VACUUMS
Why would you pretend to be scared of vacuums?
EVER SEEN A DOG DOING ANY HOUSEWORK?
HOLY SHIT
That's GENIUS
Message
Send

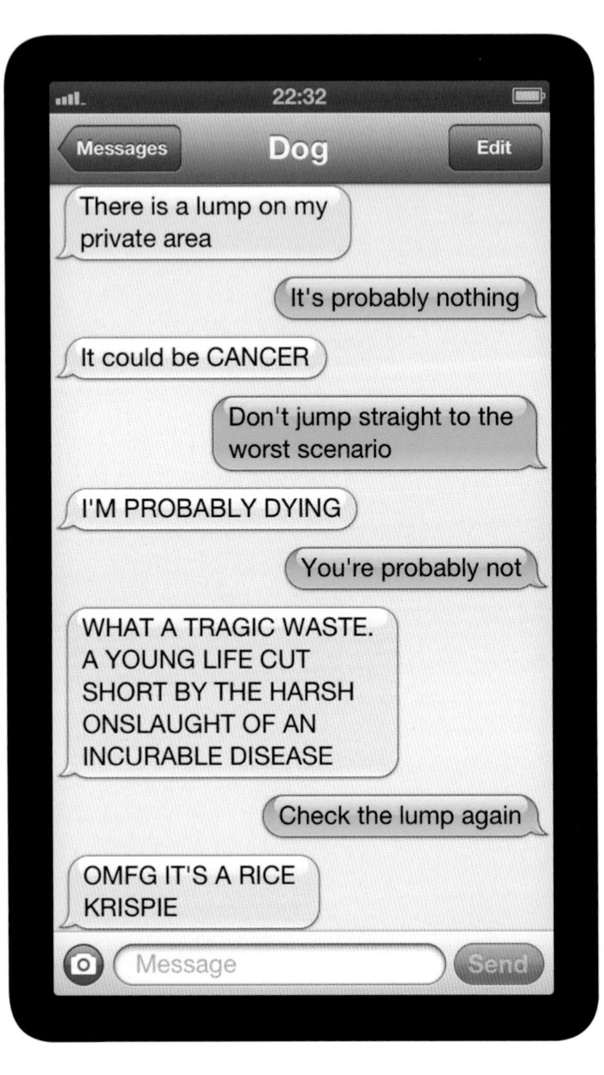
22:32
Messages
Dog
Edit
There is a lump on my private area
It's probably nothing
It could be CANCER
Don't jump straight to the worst scenario
I'M PROBABLY DYING
You're probably not
WHAT A TRAGIC WASTE. A YOUNG LIFE CUT SHORT BY THE HARSH ONSLAUGHT OF AN INCURABLE DISEASE
Check the lump again
OMFG IT'S A RICE KRISPIE
Message
Send

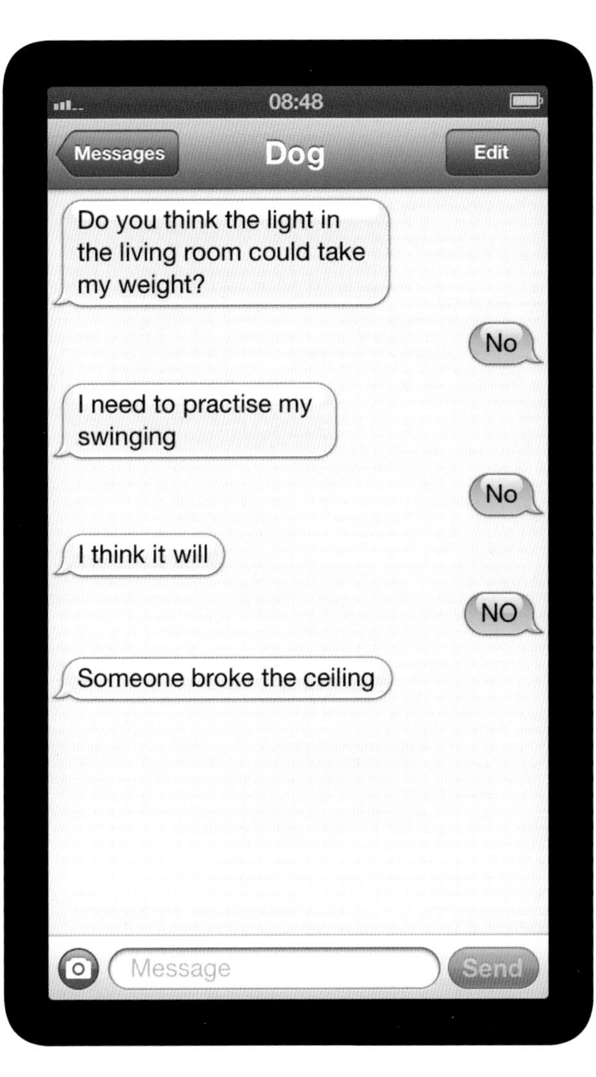
08:48
Messages
Dog
Edit
Do you think the light in the living room could take my weight?
No
I need to practise my swinging
No
I think it will
NO
Someone broke the ceiling
Message
Send

08:39
Messages
Dog
Edit
I've now urinated in EVERY SINGLE ROOM in this house
You know what that means?
No
THIS HOUSE IS MINE, BITCH
Message
Send

10:49
Messages
Dog
Edit
Cats have NINE LIVES
I know. Are you jealous?
No
Cats have nine CRAPPY LIVES
Dogs have ONE BIG AWESOME ONE
Message
Send

THE AWESOMEST

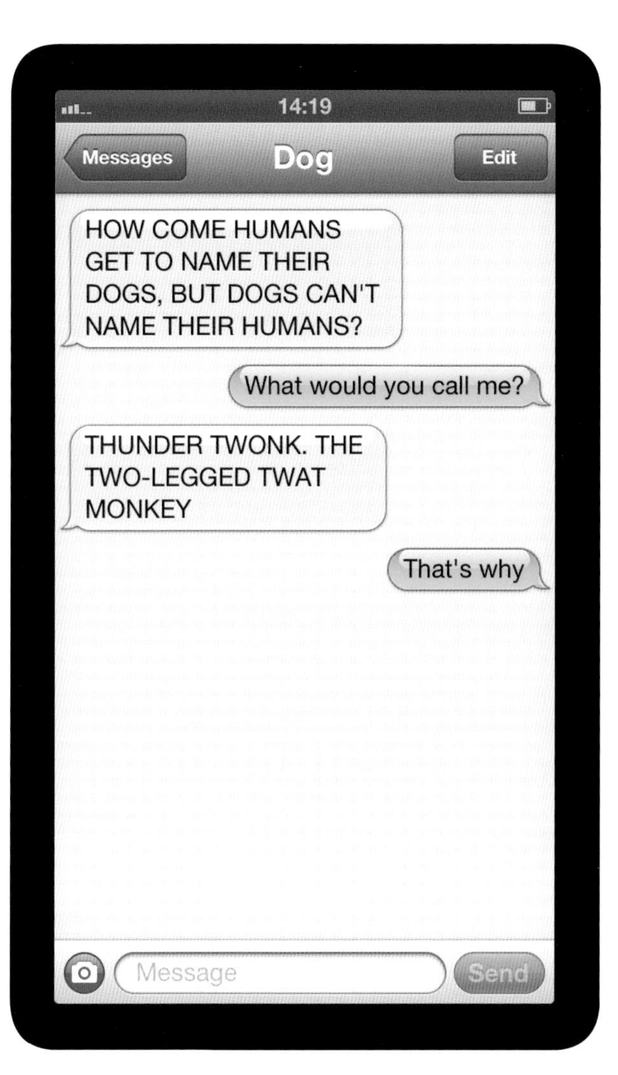
14:19
Messages
Dog
Edit
HOW COME HUMANS GET TO NAME THEIR DOGS, BUT DOGS CAN'T NAME THEIR HUMANS?
What would you call me?
THUNDER TWONK. THE TWO-LEGGED TWAT MONKEY
That's why
Message
Send

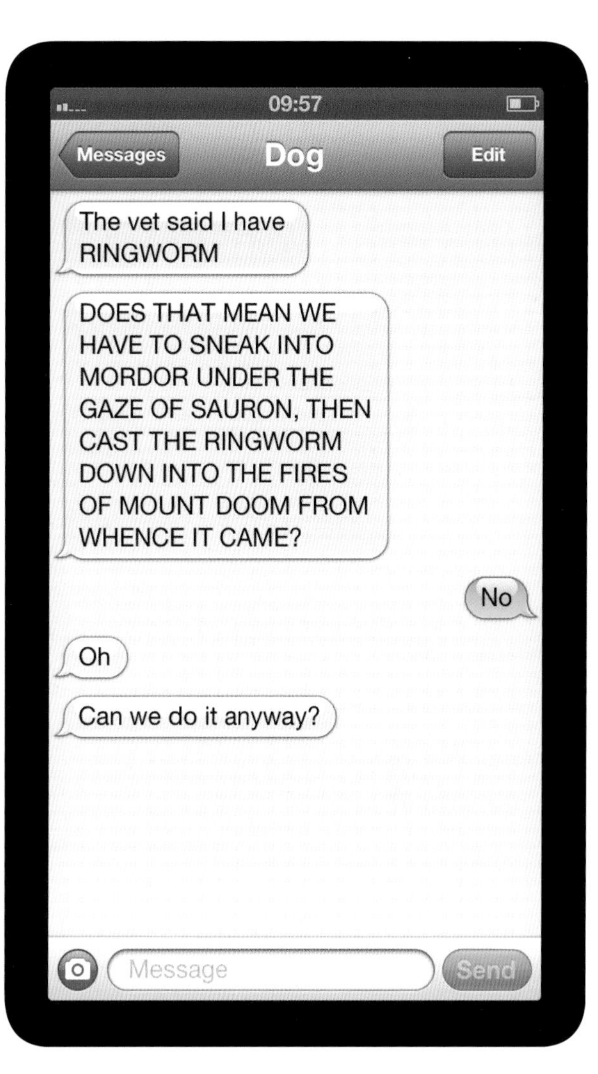
09:57
Messages
Dog
Edit
The vet said I have RINGWORM
DOES THAT MEAN WE HAVE TO SNEAK INTO MORDOR UNDER THE GAZE OF SAURON, THEN CAST THE RINGWORM DOWN INTO THE FIRES OF MOUNT DOOM FROM WHENCE IT CAME?
No
Oh
Can we do it anyway?
Message
Send

09:55
Messages
Dog
Edit
OMFG I can't hold it in any longer
Hold what in?
I have to tell you
You accidentally fed me TWICE this morning
Did I?
YEP. Once when you got up, and AGAIN before you left for work
Why didn't you tell me?
BECAUSE I GOT TWO BREAKFASTS
THIS IS THE GREATEST DAY OF MY ENTIRE LIFE
Message
Send

18:12
Messages
Dog
Edit
Your brother's here
Cool. Did you say hello to his baby? :)
Is THAT what that was?
Yes. A baby. What did you think it was?
WEIRD BALD DOG
Message
Send

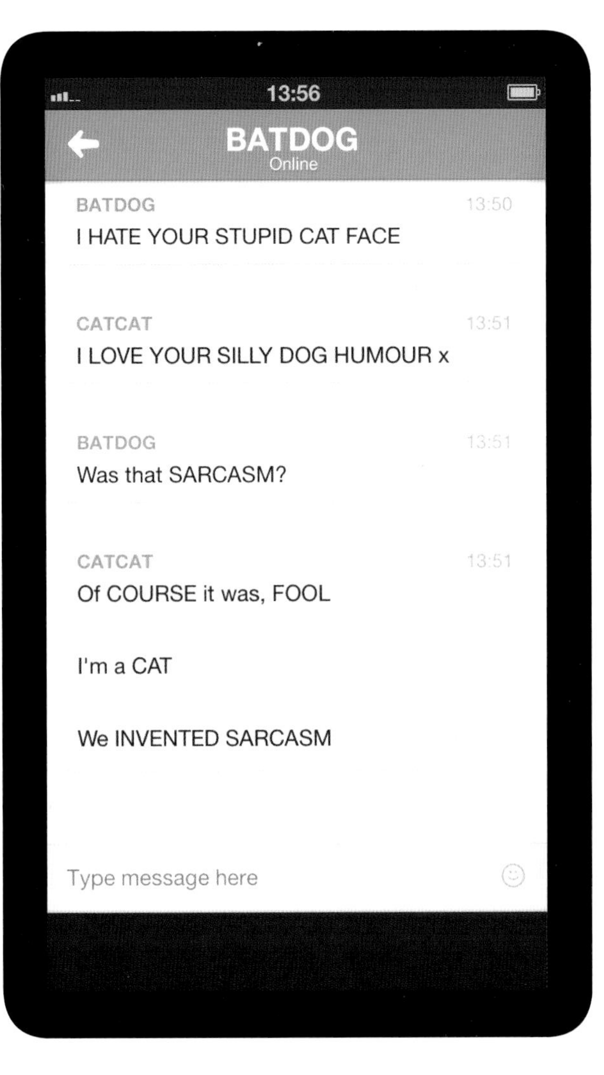
13:56
BATDOG
Online
BATDOG 13:50
I HATE YOUR STUPID CAT FACE
CATCAT 13:51
I LOVE YOUR SILLY DOG HUMOUR x
BATDOG 13:51
Was that SARCASM?
CATCAT 13:51
Of COURSE it was, FOOL
I'm a CAT
We INVENTED SARCASM
Type message here

23:18
Messages
Dog
Edit
What's it like in Dog Heaven?
There's no work. You get to do what you want ALL the time. No pressures, no responsibilities. You sleep whenever you want, and your food simply appears like MAGIC
That's pretty much the same as Dog Life
Yep. I hate you
Message
Send

22:13
Messages
Dog
Edit
I GOT BENEDICT STUCK IN A TREE
How?
I JUST TOSSED HIM UP THERE AND HE STUCK
HOW DO I GET HIM DOWN?
Throw him your phone
HAYLO HOOMAN
JUMP
Message
Send

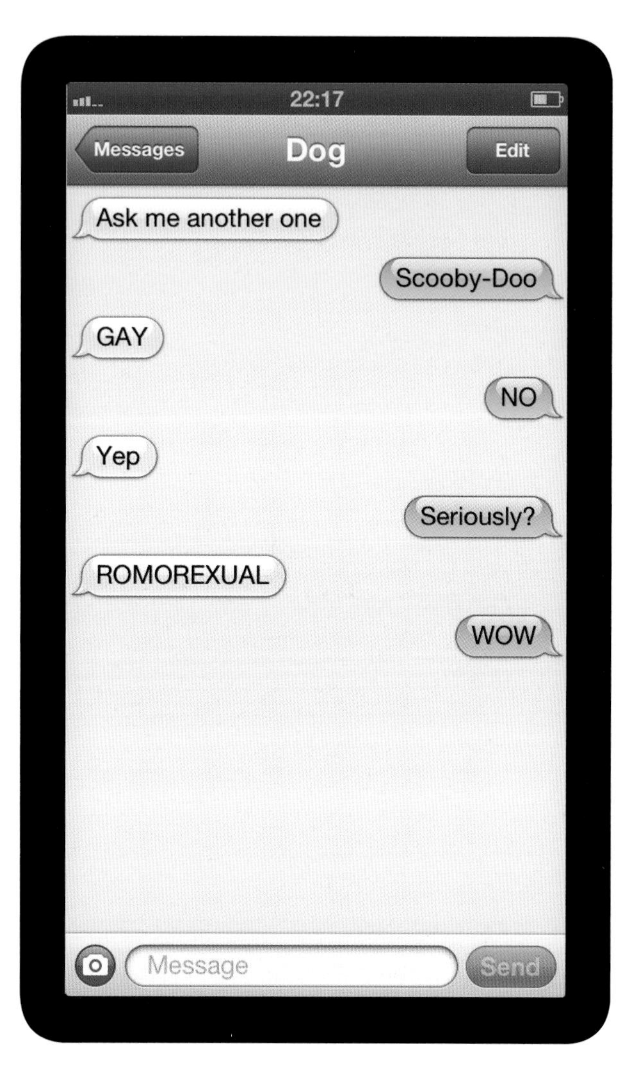
22:17
Messages
Dog
Edit
Ask me another one
Scooby-Doo
GAY
NO
Yep
Seriously?
ROMOREXUAL
WOW
Message
Send

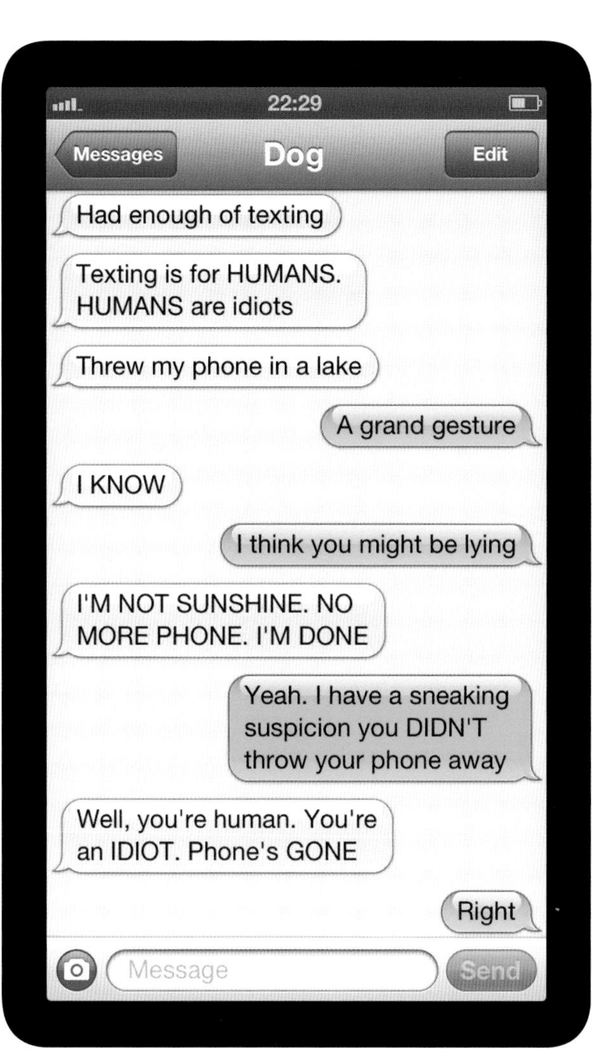
22:29
Messages
Dog
Edit
Had enough of texting
Texting is for HUMANS. HUMANS are idiots
Threw my phone in a lake
A grand gesture
I KNOW
I think you might be lying
I'M NOT SUNSHINE. NO MORE PHONE. I'M DONE
Yeah. I have a sneaking suspicion you DIDN'T throw your phone away
Well, you're human. You're an IDIOT. Phone's GONE
Right
Message
Send

07:53
Messages
Dog
Edit
Tried to build myself a new sidekick
'Build'?
I wanted to combine the power of SPEED with the power of FLIGHT
What do you mean by 'build'?
I think I misjudged the Mutation Period
EXPLAIN 'BUILD'
I PUT A PIGEON AND A SQUIRREL IN THE MICROWAVE AND THEY GOT BLOWED UP
Message
Send

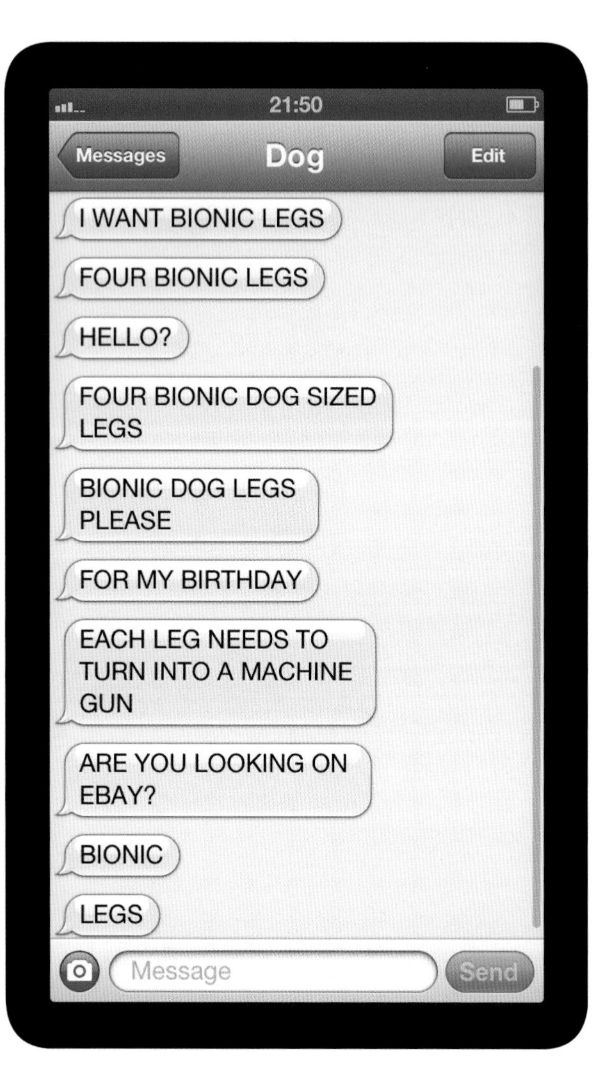
21:50
Messages
Dog
Edit
I WANT BIONIC LEGS
FOUR BIONIC LEGS
HELLO?
FOUR BIONIC DOG SIZED LEGS
BIONIC DOG LEGS PLEASE
FOR MY BIRTHDAY
EACH LEG NEEDS TO TURN INTO A MACHINE GUN
ARE YOU LOOKING ON EBAY?
BIONIC
LEGS
Message
Send

21:44
Messages
Dog
Edit
What did you want to be when you grew up?
A writer
Wow. You aimed LOW
I think it's important to be realistic
What did YOU want to be?
DOG JESUS
Message
Send

20:52
Messages
Dog
Edit
Just vommed in your new shoes. Soz x
Could you BE any more annoying?
YES
STOP EATING GRASS YOU DUMB SHIT
YOU STOP EATING GRASS
I DON'T
EXACTLY. THAT PROVES MY POINT
I'm selling you to Korea
Message
Send

10:28
Messages
Dog
Edit
FETCH THE STICK
IF I BRING IT BACK WILL YOU THROW IT AGAIN?
No
Do you PROMISE?
Yes
FETCH THE STICK
STOP TAKING ADVANTAGE OF MY TINY BRAIN AND TRUSTING NATURE
Message
Send

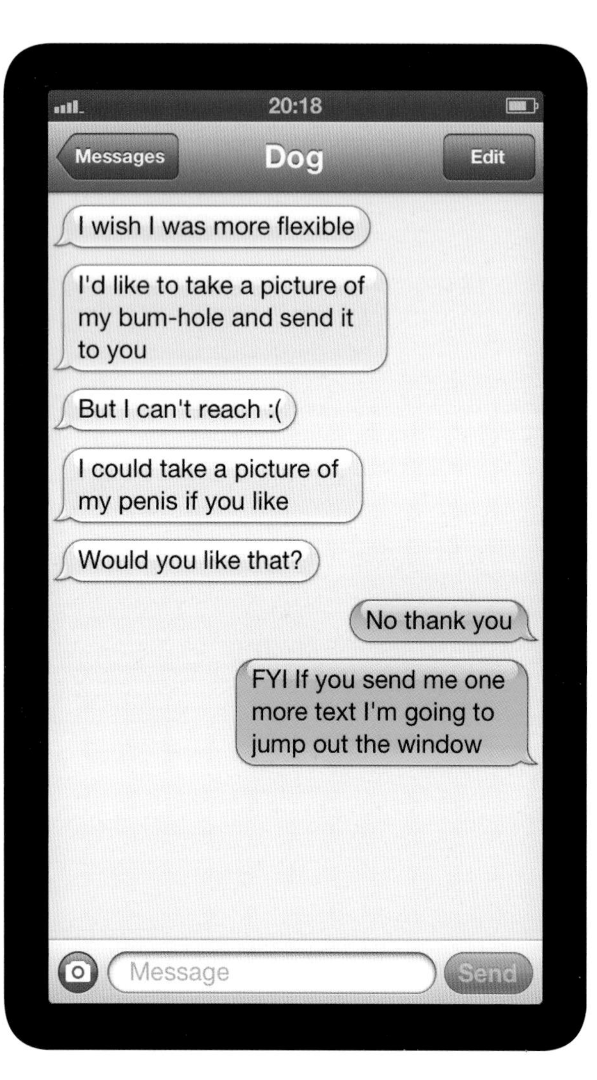
20:18
Messages
Dog
Edit
I wish I was more flexible
I'd like to take a picture of my bum-hole and send it to you
But I can't reach :(
I could take a picture of my penis if you like
Would you like that?
No thank you
FYI If you send me one more text I'm going to jump out the window
Message
Send

20:36
Messages
Dog
Edit
TELL ME A JOKE
No. You don't understand human jokes
Oh sure. Because humans are SO SMART and dogs are SO DUMB
Knock Knock
OMG SOMEONE'S AT THE DOOR BRB
Message
Send

19:28
Messages
Dog
Edit
Why did you leave me with an old man?
That's my Grandfather. It's just for tonight
He smells like A DEAD BADGER FARTED INTO A BASKET OF CHEESE
He STROKED ME and called me MARY
Yeah. That's his dead wife
OMFG How FURRY WAS YOUR NAN?
Message
Send

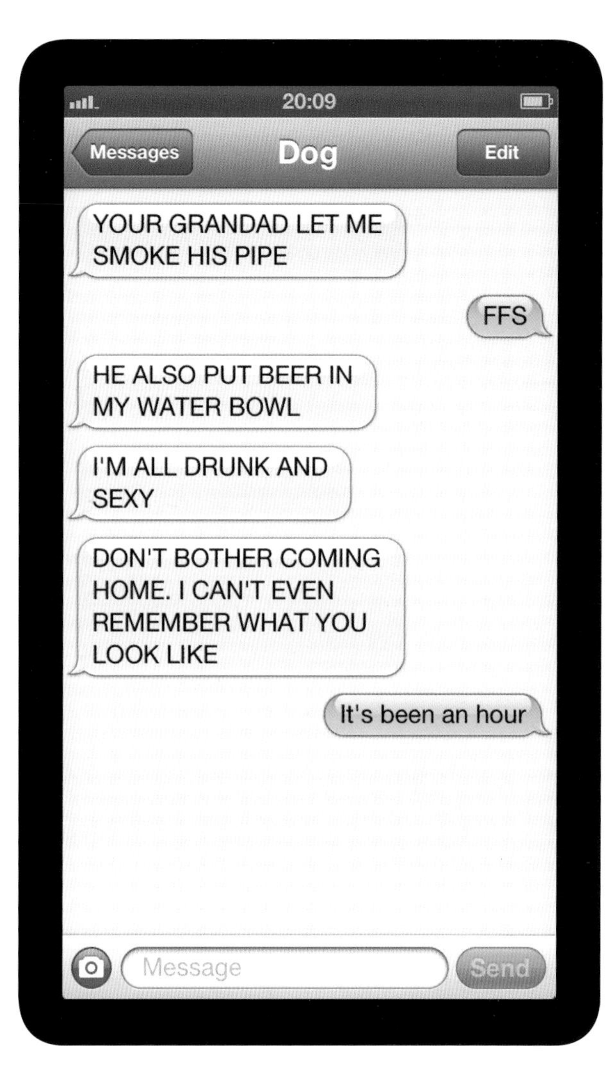
20:09
Messages
Dog
Edit
YOUR GRANDAD LET ME SMOKE HIS PIPE
FFS
HE ALSO PUT BEER IN MY WATER BOWL
I'M ALL DRUNK AND SEXY
DON'T BOTHER COMING HOME. I CAN'T EVEN REMEMBER WHAT YOU LOOK LIKE
It's been an hour
Message
Send

19:57
Messages
Dog
Edit
Are you and your girlfriend going to have a baby?
We haven't talked about it
I have the perfect name
No
It works for boys AND girls
No
YOU HAVEN'T EVEN HEARD IT YET
Fine
BATDOG
No
Message
Send

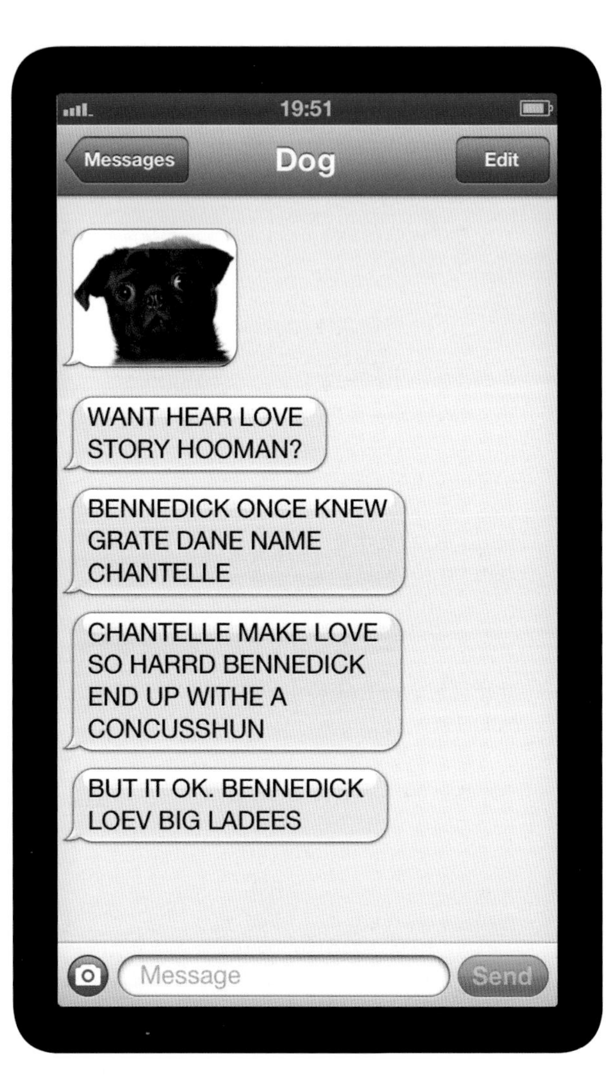
19:51
Messages
Dog
Edit
WANT HEAR LOVE STORY HOOMAN?
BENNEDICK ONCE KNEW GRATE DANE NAME CHANTELLE
CHANTELLE MAKE LOVE SO HARRD BENNEDICK END UP WITHE A CONCUSSHUN
BUT IT OK. BENNEDICK LOEV BIG LADEES
Message
Send

20:43
Messages
Dog
Edit
You cut down my bush
Yep
MY SUPER SECRET HIDEOUT BUSH
Yep
I HAD SECRET STUFF IN THERE
Two deflated balls and an old TV remote
EXACTLY. I NEEDED THOSE TO FIGHT EVIL
Message
Send

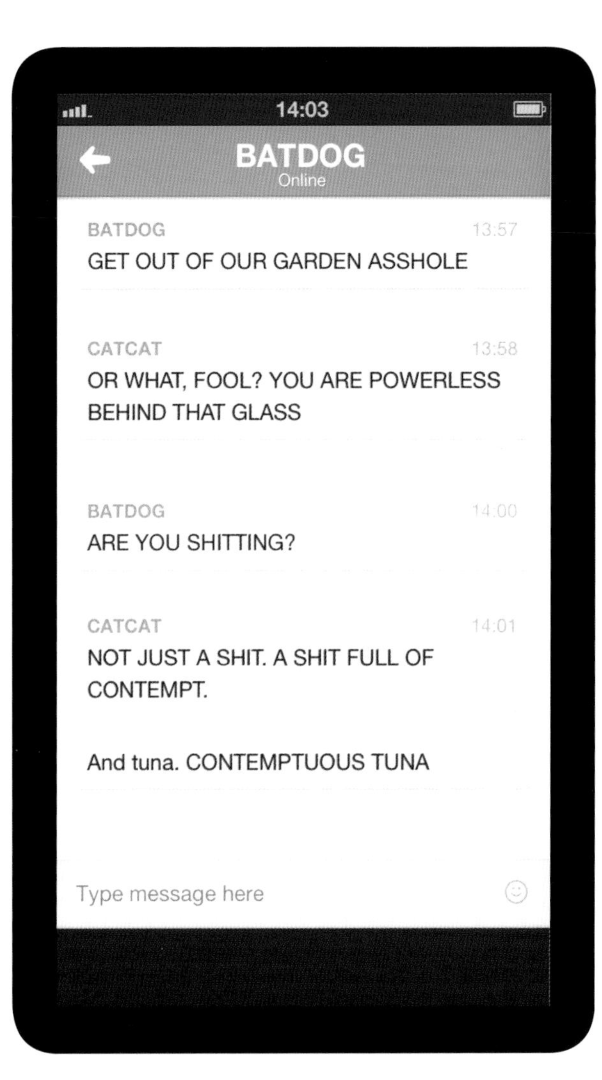
14:03
BATDOG
Online
BATDOG 13:57
GET OUT OF OUR GARDEN ASSHOLE
CATCAT 13:58
OR WHAT, FOOL? YOU ARE POWERLESS BEHIND THAT GLASS
BATDOG 14:00
ARE YOU SHITTING?
CATCAT 14:01
NOT JUST A SHIT. A SHIT FULL OF CONTEMPT.
And tuna. CONTEMPTUOUS TUNA
Type message here

23:02
Messages
Dog
Edit
BORED
Get a hobby
What's a HOBBY?
Something you do for fun
Like BREAKING stuff?
No
Like CHEWING stuff?
No
Like SHAGGING stuff?
FFS JUST STAY BORED
Message
Send

12:08
Messages
Dog
Edit
YOU THINK IT'S EASY BEING A DOG?
Yes
YOU'RE TOTALLY RIGHT. IT'S LIKE THE BEST DAY OF YOUR LIFE EVERY DAY
WHY DID YOU CHOOSE TO BE HUMAN?
Message
Send

08:25
Messages
Dog
Edit
Washed your jeans
How?
HOW did you wash my jeans?
I'm probably the most thoughtful Dog EVER
HOW DID YOU WASH MY JEANS
JESUS. I URINATED ON THEM THEN RUBBED THEM VIGOROUSLY WITH MY ENTIRE BODY
I DON'T WANT MY JEANS TO SMELL LIKE DOG PISS
WELL EXCUUUUUUUUSE ME MR FANCYPANTS
Message
Send

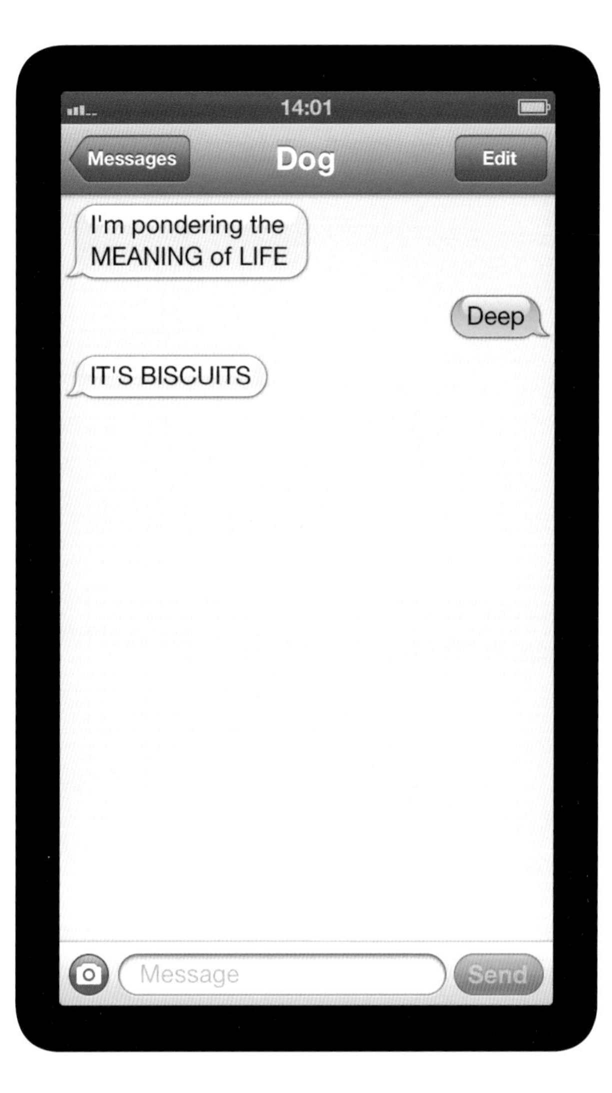
14:01
Messages
Dog
Edit
I'm pondering the MEANING of LIFE
Deep
IT'S BISCUITS
Message
Send

14:18
Messages
Dog
Edit
Are you shouting my name?
YES. STOP EATING GRASS
I wasn't
I'm at the WINDOW. I can SEE YOU EATING GRASS
HOW CAN YOU SEE ME? I'VE GOT MY EYES CLOSED
JESUS. I CAN STILL SEE YOU WHEN YOU CLOSE YOUR EYES YOU IDIOT
Holy SHIT
Message
Send

10:52
Messages
Dog
Edit
I need a new catchphrase
What was your old catchphrase?
BATDOG'S UP YOUR ASS
Hmm. That could be misinterpreted
I know. Here's my new one:
BATDOG. EXPLODING IN YOUR FACE
How about EXPLODING IN YOUR FACE WITH WHITE HOT JUSTICE
NAILED IT
Message
Send

14:26
Messages
Dog
Edit
ARE YOU NEARLY HOME?
I'm walking up to the front door right now
GOOD. I have a SURPRISE FOR YOU
For me? Aww sweet
Why did you run back outside?
That's the BIGGEST POO you've EVER done
Message
Send

11:45
Messages
Dog
Edit
IDEA: Medical drama starring a Dog surgeon. Who works in a hospital staffed ENTIRELY BY DOGS & CATS
"WHAT'S IT CALLED?" I hear you shout
I didn't
DOGTORS & PURRSES
My brain just stabbed itself to death
Message
Send

11:53
Messages
Dog
Edit
I think I've figured out a way to solve the 'Girlfriend Situation' that will make everyone happy
Go ahead
Get rid of her
That wouldn't make EVERYONE happy. That would make YOU happy
WHEN I'M HAPPY, EVERYONE'S HAPPY
THAT'S SCIENCE
Message
Send

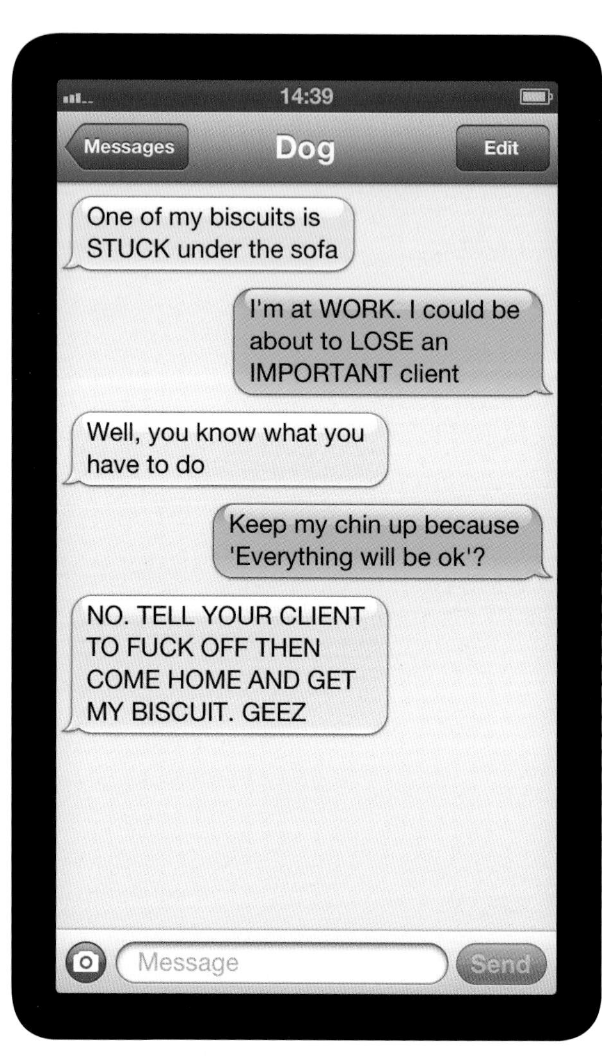
14:39
Messages
Dog
Edit
One of my biscuits is STUCK under the sofa
I'm at WORK. I could be about to LOSE an IMPORTANT client
Well, you know what you have to do
Keep my chin up because 'Everything will be ok'?
NO. TELL YOUR CLIENT TO FUCK OFF THEN COME HOME AND GET MY BISCUIT. GEEZ
Message
Send

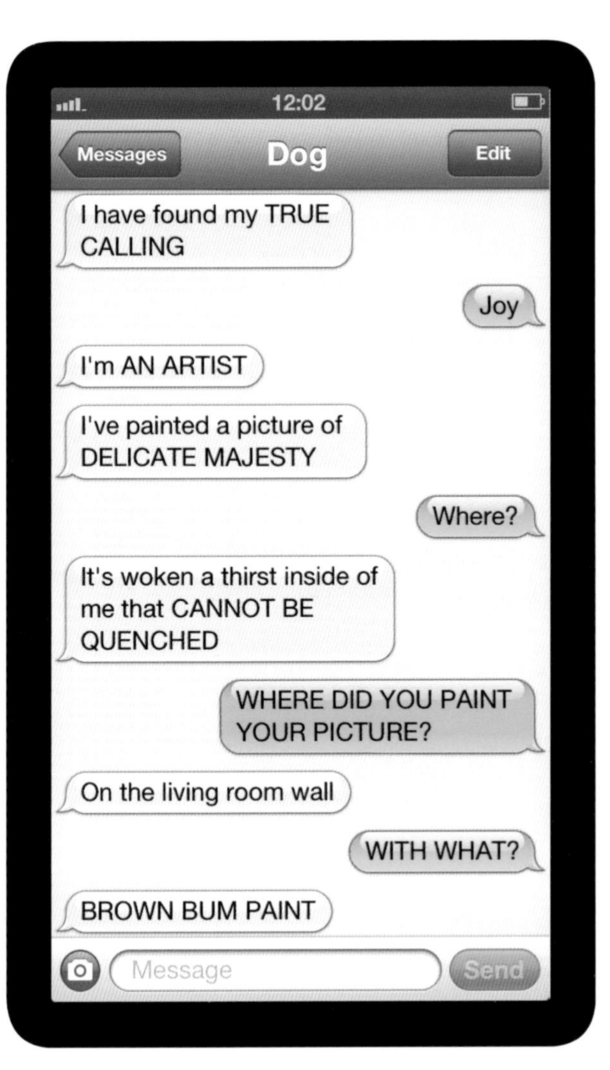
12:02
Messages
Dog
Edit
I have found my TRUE CALLING
Joy
I'm AN ARTIST
I've painted a picture of DELICATE MAJESTY
Where?
It's woken a thirst inside of me that CANNOT BE QUENCHED
WHERE DID YOU PAINT YOUR PICTURE?
On the living room wall
WITH WHAT?
BROWN BUM PAINT
Message
Send

15:00
Messages
Dog
Edit
'DOG' is 'GOD' backwards
Yep
Do you know what that means?
Nope
I MUST DESTROY THE EARTH IN SEVEN DAYS
Message
Send

15:19
Messages
Dog
Edit
Where's my new food bowl?
You don't HAVE a new food bowl
I SHOWED YOU MY NEW FOOD BOWL THIS MORNING
You showed me our neighbours' paddling pool
I EXPLAINED THIS. WE CAN FILL IT UP WHEN THE KIDS ARE AT SCHOOL
I'M NOT GOING TO FILL A PADDLING POOL WITH DOG FOOD YOU FAT BASTARD
Message
Send

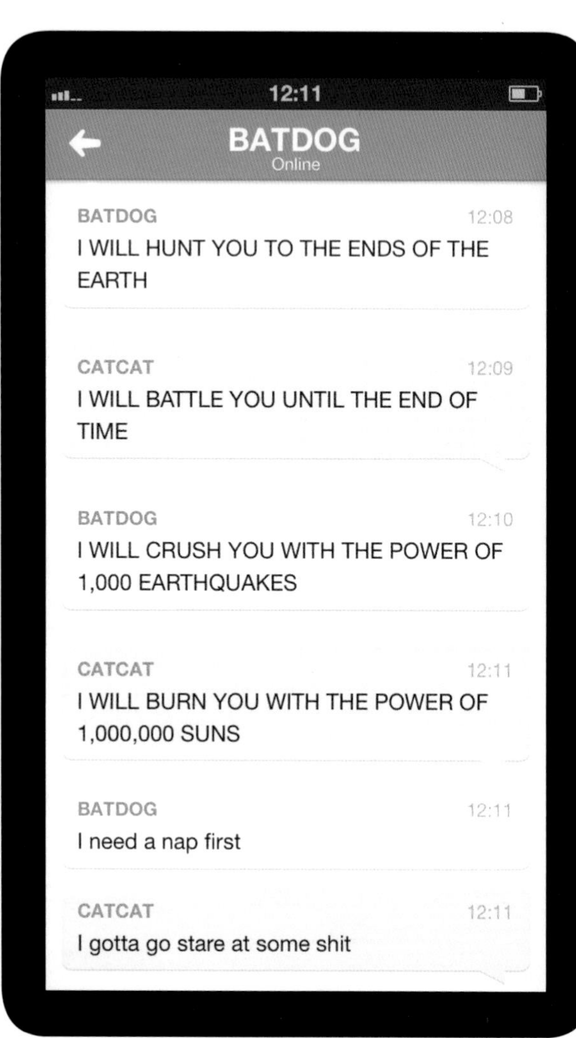
12:11
BATDOG
Online
BATDOG 12:08
I WILL HUNT YOU TO THE ENDS OF THE EARTH
CATCAT 12:09
I WILL BATTLE YOU UNTIL THE END OF TIME
BATDOG 12:10
I WILL CRUSH YOU WITH THE POWER OF 1,000 EARTHQUAKES
CATCAT 12:11
I WILL BURN YOU WITH THE POWER OF 1,000,000 SUNS
BATDOG 12:11
I need a nap first
CATCAT 12:11
I gotta go stare at some shit

15:29
Messages
Dog
Edit
Hey Twat-Monkey
Stop calling me Twat-Monkey
Hey Twat-Monkey
Stop calling me Twat-Monkey
Hey Twat-Monkey
Stop calling me Twat-Monkey
Hey Twat-Monkey
I'M YOUR MASTER. SHOW ME SOME RESPECT
HEY MR. TWAT-MONKEY
Message
Send

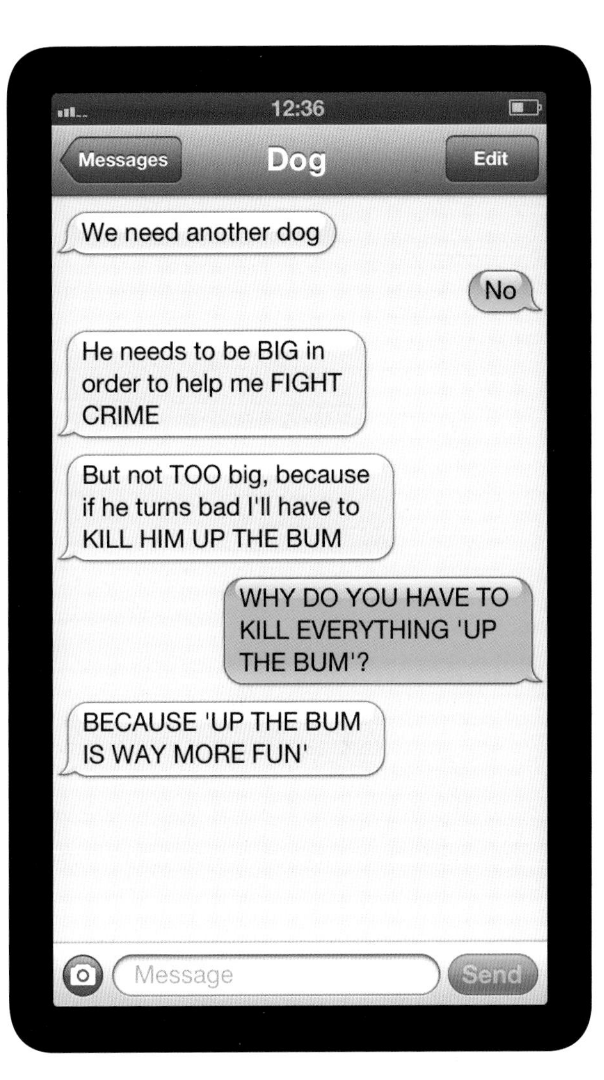
12:36
Messages
Dog
Edit
We need another dog
No
He needs to be BIG in order to help me FIGHT CRIME
But not TOO big, because if he turns bad I'll have to KILL HIM UP THE BUM
WHY DO YOU HAVE TO KILL EVERYTHING 'UP THE BUM'?
BECAUSE 'UP THE BUM IS WAY MORE FUN'
Message
Send

15:48
Messages
Dog
Edit
Tell me I look nice
What? Why?
Just tell me I look nice
You're my DOG not my WIFE
I NEED SOME POSITIVE INSPIRATION
YOU LOOK NICE
Thank you
Tell me I look nice
You look like SHIT
Message
Send

12:52
Messages
Dog
Edit
I've got a bone to pick with you
REALLY? AWESOME!
WILL THERE BE A BIG SELECTION OF BONES I CAN PICK FROM?
No, that's not what I meant
IS THERE A BONE CATALOGUE WE CAN BROWSE THROUGH?
It's a metaphor you idiot
I'M JUST GONNA PICK THE BIGGEST BONE THEY HAVE LOL
Forget it
Message
Send

13:03
Messages
Dog
Edit
I NEVER do anything RIGHT do I?
I try my BEST to be the AWESOMEST DOG EVER and all you do IS MOAN
"Don't poo in my shoes"
"Don't poo in the cupboard"
"Don't poo on the bed"
"Don't poo in my girlfriend's handbag"
You did a POO in my girlfriend's HANDBAG?
I suppose you think that's MY FAULT
Message
Send

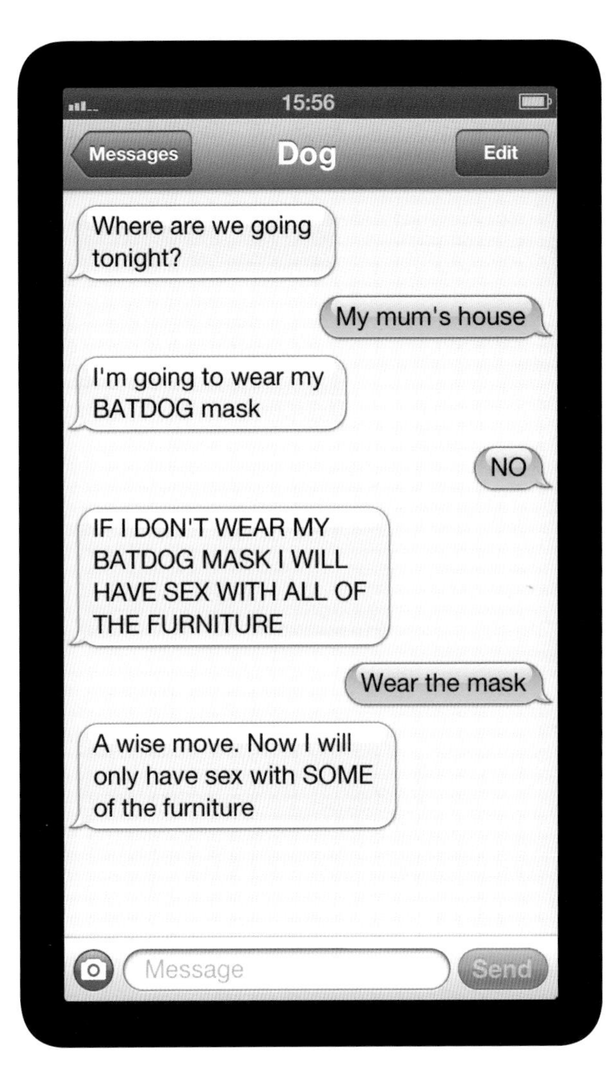
15:56
Messages
Dog
Edit
Where are we going tonight?
My mum's house
I'm going to wear my BATDOG mask
NO
IF I DON'T WEAR MY BATDOG MASK I WILL HAVE SEX WITH ALL OF THE FURNITURE
Wear the mask
A wise move. Now I will only have sex with SOME of the furniture
Message
Send

13:16
Messages
Dog
Edit
BEEN PANTING ALL MORNING
Lie down
CAN'T. STILL GOT LOADS OF PANTS TO EAT
Message
Send

16:46
Messages
Dog
Edit
Are we going to the park tonight?
Yes
Good. We can try out my new version of 'Fetch'
What's new about it?
You don't throw the stick
Ok
You put the stick DIRECTLY into my mouth
Then what?
Then you take it back out
Then we go home and watch Game of Thrones
Message
Send

13:27
Messages
Dog
Edit
JEEZ, DID YOU PUT UP ANOTHER 'MISSING' POSTER?
Yes. PEOPLE NEED TO KNOW HOW YOU TREAT ME
Message
Send

09:14
589 of 589
THIS DOG IS
MISSING
HIS BALLS
OWNER PAID VET TO CUT THEM OFF
PLEASE COME TO OUR HOUSE AND
PUNCH MY OWNER IN THE FACE
ADDRESS:

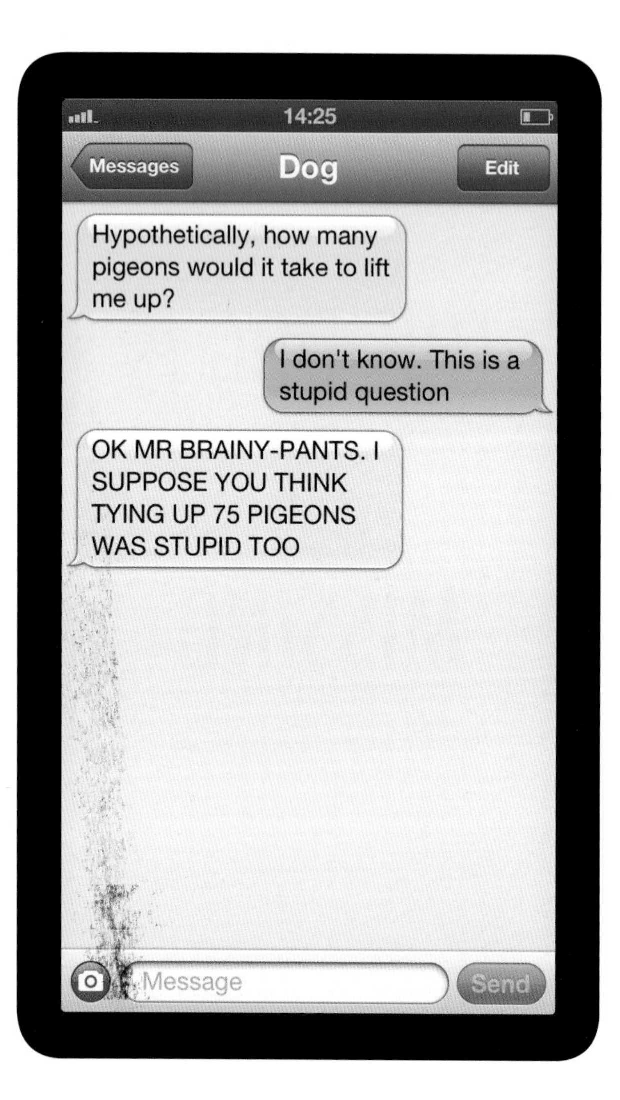
14:25
Messages
Dog
Edit
Hypothetically, how many pigeons would it take to lift me up?
I don't know. This is a stupid question
OK MR BRAINY-PANTS. I SUPPOSE YOU THINK TYING UP 75 PIGEONS WAS STUPID TOO
Message
Send

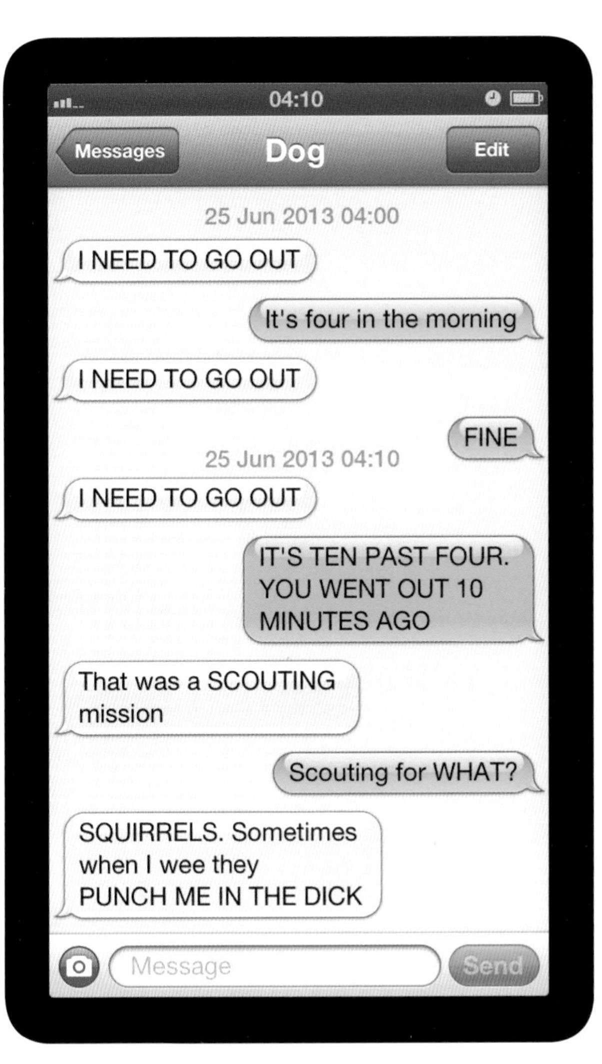
04:10
Messages
Dog
Edit
25 Jun 2013 04:00
I NEED TO GO OUT
It's four in the morning
I NEED TO GO OUT
FINE
25 Jun 2013 04:10
I NEED TO GO OUT
IT'S TEN PAST FOUR. YOU WENT OUT 10 MINUTES AGO
That was a SCOUTING mission
Scouting for WHAT?
SQUIRRELS. Sometimes when I wee they PUNCH ME IN THE DICK
Message
Send

15:24
Messages
Dog
Edit
I want a studded leather collar to make me look HARD
You'll look gay
EVEN BETTER
I WANT TO BE THE HARDEST GAYEST DOG IN THE WORLD
Message
Send

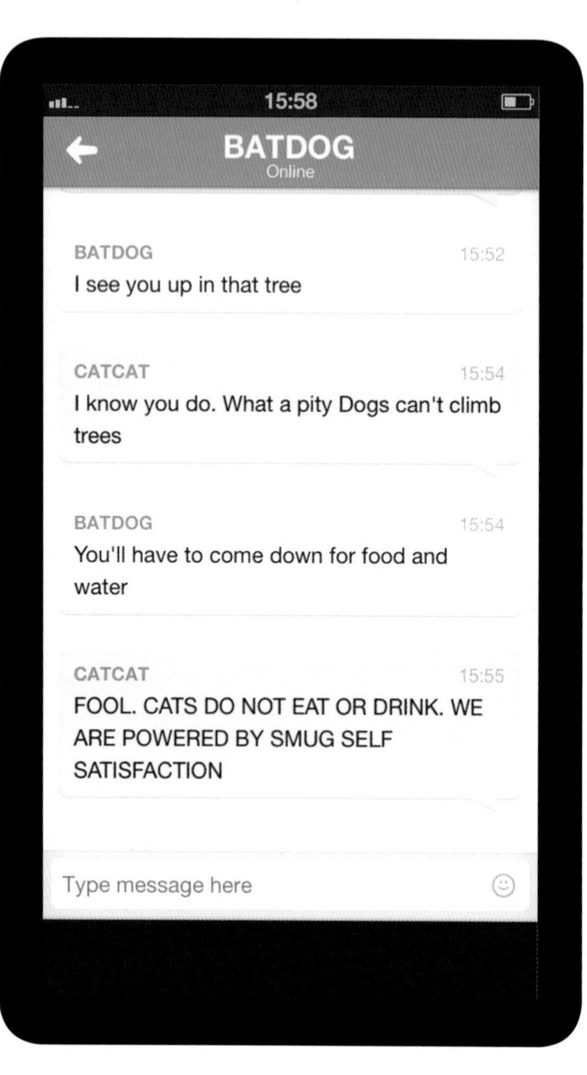
15:58
BATDOG
Online
BATDOG 15:52
I see you up in that tree
CATCAT 15:54
I know you do. What a pity Dogs can't climb trees
BATDOG 15:54
You'll have to come down for food and water
CATCAT 15:55
FOOL. CATS DO NOT EAT OR DRINK. WE ARE POWERED BY SMUG SELF SATISFACTION
Type message here

16:04
Messages
Dog
Edit
If something is 'The Dog's Bollocks' does that mean it's good?
Yes
Because Dog's Bollocks are AWESOME, right?
Yeah ok
Except mine
My bollocks are an empty sack of loneliness and BROKEN DREAMS
FFS LET IT GO
Message
Send

16:24
Messages
Dog
Edit
Tell me ONE MORE JOKE
NO
I'll GET THIS ONE
NO
PRETTY PLEASE
What do you call a fish with no eyes?
Something NICE, because that poor blind fish has probably had a VERY hard life
Forget it
Message
Send

16:34
Messages
Dog
Edit
You know which dog I hate THE MOST?
Huskies
Yes. But do you know WHY?
Because they "think they're wolves"
Have I told you this before?
YOU'VE TOLD ME EVERYTHING BEFORE
Have I told you that you look like a GIANT UGLY MONKEY MADE OF BADGER SHIT AND MOLE SPUNK?
No. That's new
Message
Send

15:38
Messages
Dog
Edit
Tell me a joke
This is the LAST TIME. If you don't get this one, you're an idiot
I'll get this one
Horse walks into a bar...
WTF? YOU TOLD ME I COULDN'T GO TO THE BAR WITH YOU BECAUSE ANIMALS AREN'T ALLOWED IN
Forget it
YOU TWAT-BITCH. I BET YOU AND THE HORSE WERE LAUGHING AT ME
Message
Send

10:35
Messages
Dog
Edit
If I run FAST enough I can TRAVEL BACK IN TIME and stop bad things from EVER HAPPENING
No you can't
ARE YOU SHITTING ME? OMFG I DID SO MUCH BAD STUFF THIS MORNING
WHAT BAD STUFF?
NOTHING. NO BAD STUFF. JUST...NEVER COME HOME AGAIN OK?
Message
Send

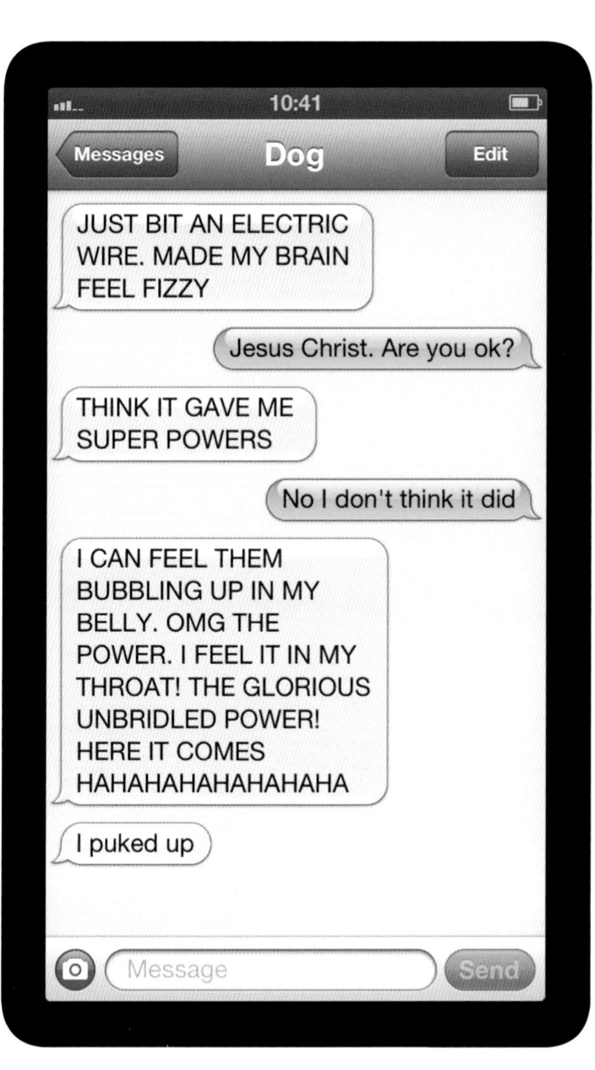
10:41
Messages
Dog
Edit
JUST BIT AN ELECTRIC WIRE. MADE MY BRAIN FEEL FIZZY
Jesus Christ. Are you ok?
THINK IT GAVE ME SUPER POWERS
No I don't think it did
I CAN FEEL THEM BUBBLING UP IN MY BELLY. OMG THE POWER. I FEEL IT IN MY THROAT! THE GLORIOUS UNBRIDLED POWER! HERE IT COMES HAHAHAHAHAHAHAHA
I puked up
Message
Send

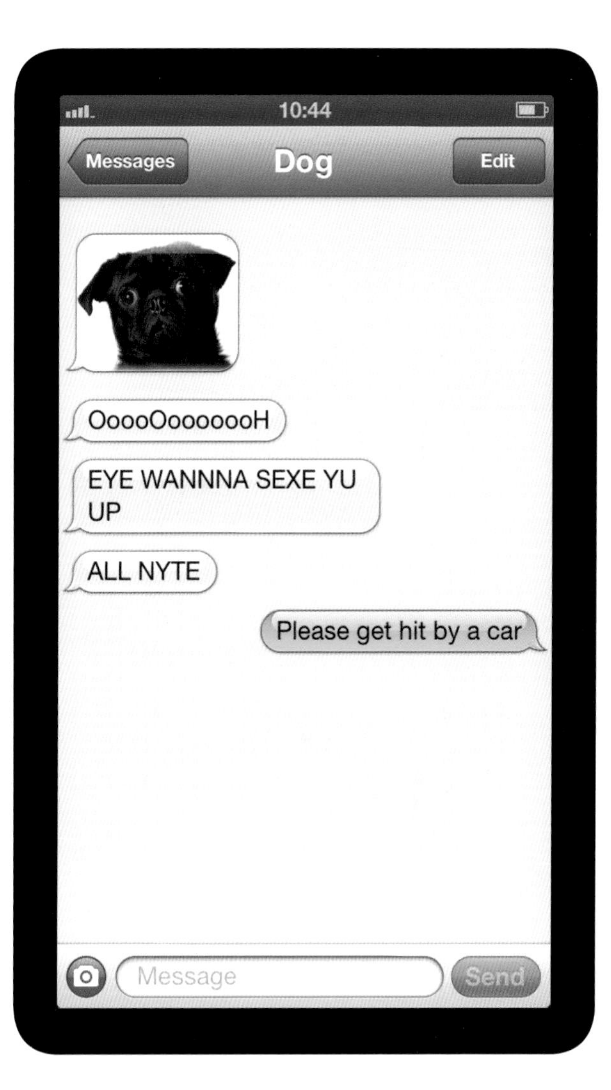
10:44
Messages
Dog
Edit
OoooOoooooooH
EYE WANNNA SEXE YU UP
ALL NYTE
Please get hit by a car
Message
Send

13:45
Messages
Dog
Edit
Will your girlfriend look after you when I die?
Yes, she will
Will she make you happy when I'm gone?
Absolutely :)
Will she get a massive tattoo of my face on her chest?
Absolutely not
FINE. I'm NEVER GOING TO DIE
Message
Send

16:40
Messages
Dog
Edit
Do you think we've learnt a lot from each other?
No
I think you've learnt a lot from ME
I already know EVERYTHING THERE IS TO KNOW
WORRY LESS
LIVE MORE
I think you're right
Of course I am. I'M BATDOG
Message
Send

DOG & I

OCTOBER JONES was born and raised in Birmingham, England, where, ironically, he spent most of his childhood terrified of dogs. This book is his second collection of text messages from his annoying Dog, Cooper. One day he hopes the voices in his head will finally stop.

DOG is the runt of a five-puppy litter born on a farm in Wales. Since the release of the first book he has become unbearable to live with. He now believes himself to be Dog Jesus, and will only eat caviar from gold plated bowls.

ACKNOWLEDGEMENTS

OCTOBER JONES: I would like to thank my family and friends for their continued support. Thank you for accepting my weirdness. Many thanks also to everyone involved at Headline.

DOG: I would like to thank myself for being so awesome. Without my canine genius, this book would not have been possible. In return for the joy I have given you, I ask for only one small thing. I would simply like to be recognised as the greatest Dog that ever lived.

Property
of
SQUIRREL
MAFIA